DATE DUE

DEMCO 38-296

FIFTY YEARS ON TRACKS

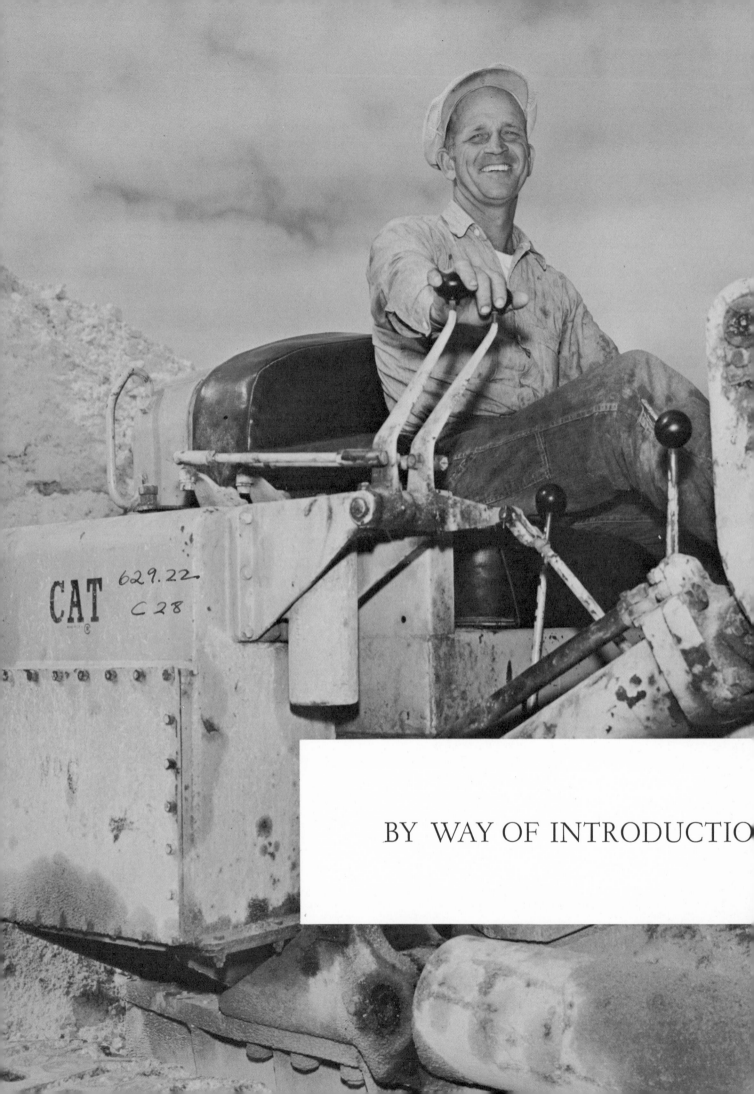

BY WAY OF INTRODUCTIO

IN 1925, the C. L. Best Tractor Co. and The Holt Manufacturing Company merged to form Caterpillar Tractor Co.; leading track-type
tractor builders of that time, the two firms had chosen an old and familiar
Holt trademark for use in their new corporate name. This anniversary book
tells the story of Caterpillar—and its important predecessors—from a beginning rooted in Nineteenth Century soil. From the vantage point of a reporter,
it presents a cross-section view of the Company today—its people, plants,
business friends, products, markets. It sketches the colorful industry of which
Caterpillar is a prominent part.

"Fifty Years on Tracks" is a tribute to the men who build roads and dams
and levees and airports . . . who till and terrace farmland and harvest its abun-
dance . . . stretch pipelines across plains and up over mountains . . . cut down
hills and erect buildings and bridges in their place . . . fell and snake logs from
the woods . . . clear roads and streets and save lives when winter comes. To the
people who build today's pyramids in months instead of decades—with
machines and free men instead of slaves by the thousands. To the workmen
who keep hammering down the cost of moving a yard of earth . . . who have
more than doubled farm output per man-hour in the last 50 years . . . who have
harnessed fuel and steel to dig more dirt, turn more wheels, pump more water,
gin more cotton, crush more stone, dig deeper wells, turn bigger propellers,
saw more wood.

Now, at the beginning of our fifty-first year of crawler tractor manufacture,
we honor these people . . . because they are our customers, yes . . . but more
properly, for the great things they have accomplished.

CATERPILLAR TRACTOR CO., PEORIA, ILLINOIS, U. S. A.

COMBINED HARVESTER

...bred in the West under the competitive leadership of two Caterpillar forerunners

The Best and Holt firms began building combined harvesters in 1885 and 1886 respectively. Benjamin Holt did not invent the combine ... but he was chiefly responsible for its early development. "So firmly established has the Holt Combined Harvester become," said the November 28, 1914, *Economist*, "that it is safe to say that 90% of the grain harvested in California, and three-quarters of all grown on the Pacific coast, pass through its capacious maw." By 1916, 6,000 Holt machines were hard at work.

Twenty-year-old Charles Holt left his New Hampshire home in 1863—bound via the Isthmus of Panama for San Francisco. There, he took on a variety of odd jobs—beginning in a local lumber yard. In 1869, he established C. H. Holt & Company, "Importers of hardwood lumber." Much of his wood was sawed at his father's New Hampshire mill—as well as the famous wagon shops of nearby Concord. Axles from Concord were held in high esteem among the trade; seasoned stagecoach drivers claimed an ability to distinguish their characteristic "sing" as they rolled over mountain roads miles from town.

During the following decade, however, it became apparent that wood products of the East did not receive proper seasoning for the hot, dry western climate. Wheels shrank, warped and fell apart under the merciless heat and sand. Charles Holt decided to manufacture his own wheels and other wagon articles at an inland West Coast location. His mechanically gifted brother, Benjamin, came west in 1883 to superintend the new Stockton, California, works.

Success did not come as quickly to Daniel Best. In 1859, age 21, he tramped west over the Oregon Trail. Bad luck hounded him for a decade as he tried gold mining, hunting and sawmilling all over the Northwest. In 1869, he took charge of his brother's ranch near Marysville, California. At the time, grain was hauled from the Best fields to town for cleaning ... the charge being three dollars per ton. Best wondered: "Why not bring the cleaner to the grain instead?" In the winter of 1869-1870, he developed and built three portable grain cleaners. During the following harvest, he and his brothers operated all three machines; Best soon opened a local factory for their manufacture.

Not long after, the young inventor moved to Albany, Oregon, and added a seed dusting machine and fanning mill to his line. He experimented with a wide variety of agricultural and general usage products, even patented a washing machine in 1877. In the early 1880s, Best moved once again—this time to Oakland, California. Business continued to boom; the company became so pressed for space that products were stored in the streets. When Oakland police objected, he looked again for a new location and chose nearby San Leandro, a few miles to the south. A Caterpillar Tractor Co. plant now stands on the same site.

Holt combine—powered by five men, 33 mules. The first "Holt Bros. Link & V-Belt Combined Harvester" appeared in 1886. In addition to combines, the 1880s saw manufacture of wagons, wheels and farm implements—not to mention railroad cars and streetcars, both horsedrawn and electric.

Best combines like these claimed
a capacity of 2,000 sacks daily.

Appearance of a photographer in the field meant a lengthy
work stoppage . . . as all hands mugged the camera. Mother
and daughter dropped harvest-time meal preparations long
enough to don their Saturday night best and get in the act.

5

Ships of the Plains

Well, old-time farmers tell us, there will never be another sight like those big old combines—far larger than those of today—looking for all the world like ships lumbering across a sea of wheat . . . tended by two-horse teams whisking away the finished grain . . . followed by every curious boy in the area . . . each boy aspiring to one of the jobs on the four-ton juggernaut.

Perhaps one coveted the job of steersman, sitting high above all atop the separator . . . guiding the machine by means of chains running to the rear of the combine tongue. Another pictured himself as driver, perched over the pilot wheel and maintaining order among the 30-odd animals out front. Or the machineman, who raised and lowered the cutting bar and ministered to the mechanical health of the machine. Or, finally, the sack sewer . . . turning the separator spout into his waiting sacks, filling them, sewing them shut and rolling them out on the stubble . . . always keeping a pile of sacks and threaded needles ready beside him.

In the 1880s, more and more marginal land came under the ambitious scrutiny of the farmer. His eyes turned to the foothills and rolling meadows with which California abounds. These knew no plow and had felt, if anything at all, only the hooves of Spanish and pioneer American cattle. The combine had proven ineffective on these fertile hills. Grain grew well enough . . . but in a tilted combine, it moved too fast or too slow and bunched up in the corners of the machine.

In 1891, Benjamin Holt introduced his sidehill harvester, probably the first one to achieve any continued commercial success. Now, for the first time, the harvester could go anywhere a team could go—and still operate efficiently. Profitable grain farming became a reality on hundreds of thousands of sloping untilled acres across the Pacific Northwest.

Best sidehill harvester. Both Holt and Best machines were of the "pulled" type and cost about $1.25–$1.50 per acre to operate—including maintenance, depreciation, labor and horses.

Holt self-propelled sheet metal harvester (1913). The company turned out its first self-propelled harvester model two years earlier.

sidehill combines—like these—helped boost Washington wheat production from six million bushels in 1890 to 42 million in 1920.

Holt purchased this company in 1901, continuing its line of combines, plows and other farm tools. Several similar firms were acquired in the 1894–1908 period.

7

BIG STEAM

. . . combines and tractors of a size to make even today's largest look small . . . . .

Combined harvesters got bigger and bigger. Some required as many as 40 horses to pull. And in the delta areas, horses sank deeply into the soil and churned up the soft ground. Farmers wanted more power—compact power—that would ride on top of the soft land. Was steam the answer? The Best and Holt companies led the West Coast during the Big Steam Era, 1890–1910. With giant steam power, daily harvest totals occasionally ran to 125 acres and 4,000 bushels.

Daniel Best delivered his first steam harvester in February, 1889, for $4,500 . . . then stayed on for one week to instruct the new owner. The machine had two sections: traction engine and combine. The two traction engine drive wheels were eight feet high and 26 inches across. Great wheel size helped the machine get over logs and up out of holes . . . in addition to distributing the 11-ton weight over a larger area. Straw, wood or coal served as fuel. Six men were needed: an engineer and fireman for the traction engine . . . one sack sewer, header tender and overseer . . . and one man and a team to draw wood and water behind. The rig cut a swath of 25 feet, ran three miles per hour and harvested from 65 to 100 acres daily. Best claimed it would do the work of 75 mules for the cost of the barley consumed.

Steam, of course, was nothing new. The heavy, snorting, clanking machines had been lumbering across American farmfields since the 1850s. But in spite of this apparent popularity, the steam tractor never threatened the reign of the horse in open field work. True, it was both powerful and mechanically simple. But for combining, it offered little in the way of man-hour savings over big-horse methods. It presented a definite fire problem. It was unwieldy, heavy—sometimes over 20 tons. In the hands of a careless operator, it could be dangerous.

In 1890, Benjamin Holt turned out his first steamer. In the following 24 years, Holt built 130 wheel-type steam traction engines. Beginning with shipment of a combine to Australia in 1894, the Holt firm did an exceptional job of developing foreign markets. In 1904, the King of Spain glimpsed one of the "immense American affairs" near Seville . . . then hinted he would like a small model at his court. Holt mechanics went to work and shipped a miniature traction engine and combine early the following year.

Holt 60 horsepower steamer hauling up 10% grade.

Logging the western woods . . . 1894 style.

Holt steam traction engine and 50-foot-cut combine—complete with American flag—built in 1893.

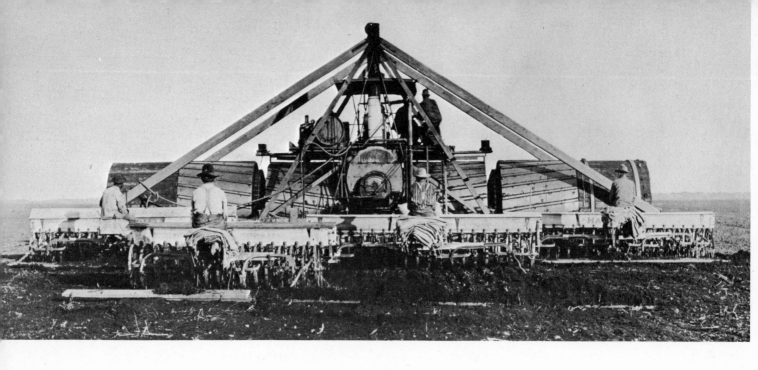

Stupendous, Tremendous, Colossal . . .

Top photograph: Almost 46 feet of tractor...working in California's San Joaquin Valley. Each of the six wheels was 7½ feet in diameter and six feet wide. Holt built the machine shortly after the turn of the century; then added the extra wheels to keep it on top of the soft ground. The behemoth worked well enough on the straight-away . . . but was difficult to turn and impossible to get through fence rows and across bridges and roads. Below: The last word in big wheels . . . built by Daniel Best in 1900 for the Middle River Farming Co. of Stockton. The 20-ton machine had wood covered drive wheels 15 feet wide and nine feet in diameter.

Engineer and fireman on Holt freighting model fitted with headlight.

Holt steam traction engine in Kenya, Africa . . . about 1903.

Three Best rigs for California copper mining . . . about 1904.

11

BIRTH OF THE CRAWLER

. . . from big steam and big wheels, a revolutionary idea

How to reconcile big power and big weight with soft land? As capacity of the steam traction engine climbed, weight increased accordingly. And as weight increased, wheels mired even deeper into California delta soil.

At first, both Best and Holt had attacked the problem by adding larger wheels—and more of them—to increase the bearing area of their tractors on the soft earth. The resulting machines were expensive, unwieldy. The need was evident: more traction through greater ground contact area . . . yet with compactness and better maneuverability. These considerations brought Benjamin Holt around to the idea of a "treadmill" type of machine to pick up and lay its own broad base as it traveled . . . as if it were a portable railroad.

The concept of such a vehicle was hundreds of years old. Thousands of drawings had been made. Inventors had filed over 100 patents—including one juggernaut that was to have a main frame more than 50 feet in width, be powered by two steam engines and function as a combination plow, harrow, seeder and harvester. Other inventors had previously built several track-type machines. None was practical enough to achieve continuing commercial significance.

Holt did not immediately see the great potential of his tracklaying idea. The few men working on the project counted it only a day's work and scarcely thought the idea would be multiplied hundreds of thousands of times. The new track structure was intended simply as a solution to a very bothersome local problem . . . that of keeping machines on top of the rich but spongy peat soil just west of Stockton. This land, especially during the winter rainy season, was so soft that a conventional traction engine would quickly sink down in it.

Testing of the first crawler occurred on Holt property in this region; Holt steam traction engine No. 77 wheeled its last on the way to the site. There, wheels were removed and a pair of the new track units installed. The result was the world's first practical track-type tractor—tested November 24, 1904. Here was a 40 horsepower machine that pulled four gangs of plows two inches deeper than the Holt 60 horsepower wheel model pulled three similar gangs!

The test was described the following spring by *Farm Implement News:* "In a tract where a man could not walk without sinking to his knees and where tule-shod horses could not be used . . . the new traction engine was operated without a perceptible impression in the ground . . . This tract of land has been useless for crop raising for several years because no way was found to plow it, but the platform wheel engine has brought the land into use again . . . it is predicted that with the new device it will be possible to work any of the soft lands of the reclaimed districts and bring into cultivation thousands of acres of rich areas that are now unproductive."

Beginning with steam traction engine No. 77, Holt removed the wheels . . . and replaced them with a pair of tracks. Each track frame was 30 inches high, 42 inches wide and nine feet long. Tracks themselves were 3" x 4" wooden slats. Holt figured the tracks had as much bearing surface as wheels 75 feet in diameter.

First regular production model crawler . . . sold in 1906 to the Golden Meadow Developing Co. for use in Louisiana delta lands. Price—$5,500.

NEW MODELS...NEW MARKETS

...the results of gasoline power and a new Peoria factory.....

After 1900, the gasoline engine moved quickly to the front. True, steam had offered a certain compactness and simplicity. But it brought little in the way of savings over big horse hitches. It was a constant fire hazard. It was heavy, unwieldy, cumbersome.

Both Daniel Best and Benjamin Holt started work on gasoline power in the 1890s. By 1895, Best was advertising the superiority of his gas engine over conventional steam power...lower fuel cost, less fire risk, less heat, far less space, quicker starting and stopping, and elimination of both boiler and fireman. His five horsepower engine, he said, would run 10 hours on 48¢ worth of crude oil. In the summer of 1896, Best sponsored a tug-of-war between an experimental gasoline tractor and one of his steamers; the newer model, according to the *San Leandro Reporter*, "hauled the steam engine around the block."

As more farmers settled the West, increasing numbers could justify use of a combined harvester but not a steam traction engine. Accordingly, Benjamin Holt tested the application of auxiliary gasoline combine power in the 1890s. The sale of one such model in 1904 marked an important advance in combine progress.

Quickly admitting the shortcomings of steam, Holt built an experimental gasoline crawler in 1906. First production model went to work on the Los Angeles Aqueduct in 1908. Winding 233 miles across the Mojave Desert and the foothills of the Tehachapi Mountains in southern California, the aqueduct was a real challenge to the new machine. Los Angeles bought one, then two more...then 25 the following year. By the beginning of 1910, over 100 Holt crawlers were in operation. Development of the machine boomed Holt employment from 300 in 1909 to 1,000 in 1914.

In the meantime, in 1909, Holt acquired a plant in Peoria, Illinois. The first Peoria tractor, assembled the same year, went to nearby Bloomington, Illinois... where the buyer refused to pay for the new contraption until its ability to perform was a fact.

The easterly move was a fortunate one for the big West Coast tractor builder. Peoria boasted a central location, good rail and waterways service, a skilled labor supply. The city was already a heavy manufacturing center. Production of plows, fanning mills and simple agricultural tools dated back to the early 1840s. Agricultural and earthmoving tools had always been one of the town's leading industries. By the end of 1910, the Holt riverside plant claimed 65 employees working for an average of 25¢ hourly.

Peoria's "California Caterpillar Gasoline Traction Engine."

Single cylinder Best gas engine powering bean cleaner, 1895.

Holt's new gasoline crawler lumbers uphill in a public demonstration, 1908.

Holt steam-type crawler hauling Marion Shovel on Los Angeles Aqueduct Project, 1908.

A double header on the Mojave Desert. Construction of Los Angeles Aqueduct, 1909.

15

Holt "60" pulling gravel wagons in Michigan, 1911. Short haul freighting was an excellent crawler market.

Selling the Crawler

How to sell a machine that most farmers had never even seen? Should dealers be used? Branch houses? Direct selling from the factory? What about commissions and discounts? The market was ripe enough. The great need was for salesmanship—persuasive, yes, but primarily educational—with a strong training and service follow-up after each sale. Letters from field people bewailed the ineptness of "numbskulls" running the tractors.

Most sales before World War I were direct, with agent or dealer sometimes participating as a casual factor. Sales handled through agents were generally accomplished on a loose basis. Some few were progressive and large enough to merit a fixed commission of from 5 to 20% of all sales in a given territory. Others simply received a flat commission or fee for each machine sold. Still another factor was the "booster" or "bird dog" who was commissioned to provide sales leads to dealer or manufacturer.

Crawler prices generally fell between $2,500 and $5,000. But final price depended upon the number of tractors in the yard. Chief buyer was the large grain farmer. Chief competition was the horse, mule and mule skinner. Tractor makers handled their own financing. When a machine was sold, typically, the builder took 30 or 40 mules plus harness as down payment. The trick was to sell the mules at a good price before they ate up the profits. Subsequent farmer payments usually followed each crop year.

Salesmen talked the most about crawler versatility . . . as compared with horses, mules and "round wheel" tractors. In 1915, one customer won a solid gold watch fob for submitting the most uses for his machine in a Holt-sponsored contest. Among the winning 40 uses were: "pulling a horse out of dug well, moving house, sawing wood, breaking mules to lead and accustom them to machinery, pulling steam engine out of mud hole, pulling automobile out of mud hole, using in place of gate when gate was broken."

This "30" carried the familiar "Caterpillar" trademark . . . originated by Holt and applied to products of the Holt line.

This Holt "45" appeared at the Panama-Pacific Exposition in 1915. Customers called it a "muley" (no front wheel).

Demonstrating that their machine didn't need a front tiller wheel for steering, Holt engineers simply cut it out.

In 1917, Toonerville Trolley's famous creator suggested the crawler principle as a commuter's answer to muddy roads.

First Best Tracklayer—the "75"—1913.

New Company, Old Name

The early Best and Holt firms were keenly competitive . . . with Best leaning more to the steam tractor business and Holt to the combine trade. Best sold out to The Holt Manufacturing Company in 1908. But only two years later, the rivalry was renewed. Beginning at a plant in Elmhurst, California, Daniel Best's son organized the C. L. Best Gas Traction Co., principally for the manufacture of wheel-type tractors. He moved back to his father's old San Leandro location a few years later.

In 1913, the young man turned also to the crawler idea, presented his "75" Tracklayer and advertised that his "Self-Laying Track, by increasing the surface area, absolutely eliminates any danger of soil packing and enables the tractor to travel on any ground." Early machines were billed as "all steel." Though not strictly accurate, this was truer of the Tracklayer than of any other make. Best soon claimed a share of Holt leadership in the track-type tractor field.

Best "Humpback 30" plowing a walnut orchard, 1915.

Two Holt "75s" working near Surabaya, Java, 1915.

Export Horizons

By January, 1915, over 2,000 Holt crawlers were at work for their owners. One leading reason was the device's sale and acceptance in over 20 foreign lands.

In late 1910, a prosperous Hungarian landowner chanced upon an American farm publication describing Holt's Caterpillar track-type Tractor. Leo Steiner gathered that the "engine rolls like a railway car on an endless self-laying track instead of on wheels." A year later, Steiner had a Holt "60" working his huge farm. Within another year, he had become Holt's first European dealer and had placed orders for 40 machines.

Also in late 1910, a member of the Holt company freighted a crawler to the Argentine, demonstrated for several months and established a dealer there. The new Argentine dealer succeeded so well in popularizing the machine that a standing monthly order of 15 tractors followed. In 1911, this business was shifted to Peoria and soon absorbed most of the productive capacity of the new factory.

1912 . . . Dealer Leo Steiner demonstrates near Budapest.

Early Holt crawler sold to Pioneer Mining of Nome, Alaska.

Horse-drawn blade grader, 1910 road grading job.

Horse *vs.* Tractor

The Holt company was among the first to twist old Dobbin's tail. "Possibly some farmers keep their horses for sentimental reasons," said Holt's magazine, *Caterpillar Times.* "If so, well and good. The horse has been a good friend, so keep him, if you wish, as a matter of kindness. It's an expensive proposition, to be sure, but sentiment excuses many luxuries."

The horse, said Holt salesmen, is out of step with progress. His is the poorest engine ever built. For every hour he works, he eats 10 pounds of food; his thermal efficiency is only two per cent. You can't keep a horse busy the year around; he averages only 3½ hours of work each day and isn't up to really heavy tasks. He needs one acre out of five for feed and costs $100 a year to maintain.

Tractors, on the other hand, don't need to be rested in hot weather . . . are not "soft" in the spring when needed most . . . are not subject to flies, bees and sickness . . . need no barns, only a shed . . . don't "eat" fuel when idle . . . require fewer men to operate and maintain . . . will do heavier work longer . . . keep busier the year around . . . make for better crops, better

profits, better living standards. When the Boston Work Horse Relief Association mailed out a set of 12 detailed horse handling rules, Holt reprinted all 12 and added No. 13; "If you have freighting, or harvesting, or plowing or heavy tractive work that must be done in hot weather, cold weather or any other kind of weather, don't depend on horses at all, but get a Caterpillar crawler Tractor . . . This will, moreover, relieve you from observing all the other 12 cautions listed above."

The Holt company used poetry as well as prose:

The horse is sliding off the map; his friends at last admit it.
He'll hang around a while mayhap, but soon he'll have to quit it.
For things propelled with gasoline increase each day in numbers,
And Dobbin leaves this earthly scene for his eternal slumbers.

Horse advocates, however, took none of this lying down. Said a 1915 farm journal:

I'll let my neighbor fret and stew about the things his tractor'll do;

I'll take old Dan and Kate and Ned, and hitch them to a plow instead.

Let neighbor plow with his machine and raise his corn with gasoline;
My way of farming is the best; I have more time to smoke and rest.

Tractors, thundered the Percheron Society of America, the Horse Association of America and others, tractors are taking the romance and spiritual rewards out of farming. They're undermining the Nation's morals. They're bad for the land. They're ruining the farmer.

In the latter respect, at least, horse associations had something of a point. By 1917, under the impetus of war and a burgeoning market, tractors bore the names of more than 200 firms—or over five times as many as today. Builders vied with each other in a frantic race for sales. In many areas, unlimited credit was the rule. Generally, quality was poor. For most makes, service

didn't exist. Internal engine wear from dirt became so acute that many farmers turned back to steam. Certain areas were glutted with rusting tractors—some simply no good in the first place and others not usable for want of a part.

The now famous Nebraska Tests were originated by the 1919 Nebraska Legislature "to provide official tests for gas, gasoline, kerosene, distillate or other liquid fuel traction engines . . . and to compel the maintenance of adequate service stations for same."

The outcome, however, was never in doubt. By 1925, tractors were over the half-million mark. Horse and mule population had fallen from a peak of 26.7 million to 22.6 million; by 1940, to 14 million; by 1952, to 6.3 million. Work horse quality slipped as breeding and training were de-emphasized. Tractors soared over the million mark by 1935; about 2½ million were on farms at the close of the Second World War. A post-war boom has almost doubled that number.

Elevating grader pulled by a Caterpillar "60" Tractor, 1913. One of the first roadbuilding machines to be principally crawler powered, the elevating grader both dug and cast earth as it traveled. The elevating grader pictured here and the blade grader on the opposite page were products of the Russell Grader Manufacturing Company of Minneapolis. Organized in 1903, Russell helped pioneer the development of graders (both drawn and self-propelled), scrapers, portable crushers and other road machinery. It became part of Caterpillar Tractor Co. in 1928.

One-bottom plow and two-horse team. Production—about two acres per nine-hour day.

Predecessor to the logging arch and sulky—slip-tongue wheel and four-horse team.

Drag scraper and teams, World War I period. For a haul of 500 feet, each rig moved about 10 cubic yards of earth daily.

22

Bulldozer, 1917 . . . built for filling ditches and marshes and spreading dirt after wagons dumped it.

The new and old: Best Sixty and elevating grader loading horse-drawn wagon . . . 1920.

BIRTH OF THE TANK

Tanks were first employed by the Allies between the Somme and the Ancre in September, 1916, at Malmaison and Cambrai in 1917. They were yet to perform at Chateau-Thierry and Reims, Amiens, St. Mihiel, and in the Meuse-Argonne campaign that spelled "checkmate" to the Germans. Meantime, everybody wondered. Where were the enemy tanks? Had German engineers overlooked military refinement of an American invention—the track-type tractor?

Evidently so. According to General S. D. Rockenbach, World War I chief of the U. S. Tank Corps, only 15 German-made tanks saw action throughout the entire course of the war. None was placed in the field before 1918. How did it happen that the Germans fell behind so completely? Was it because they had no previous opportunity to witness the American crawler in action? History says no.

First real Allied interest began in 1914 when British Lt. Colonel (later Major General) E. D. Swinton proposed construction of an armed "land destroyer" on a Caterpillar track-type Tractor base. First Lord of the Admiralty Winston Churchill followed with a recommendation urging "special mechanical devices" for crossing trenches. Yet long before, in 1912, in the Austro-Hungarian monarchy, enemy military leaders looked on as the same machine demonstrated its crawling and pulling power. This "traction trial," arranged by Holt dealer Leo Steiner, took place on loose, sandy Hungarian terrain. Impressed, the monarchy's war department expressed confidence, even asked Steiner to manufacture the machine in Austria.

Expecting the German War Department to be fully as enthusiastic, Steiner scheduled a 1913 demonstration near Magdeburg. He writes: "I was completely bewildered when I received the (Germans') answer: 'We are not interested in this engine. It is of no importance for military purposes.' This statement stood in direct opposition to the attitude of the Austro-Hungarian War Department. I have the impression that the bitter rivalry between the two departments induced . . . this foolish judgment, which later proved to be one of the most fatal errors in their history."

In the meantime, the British moved quickly with military adaptation of the "Yankee machine that climbs like hell." The first "land destroyers" were assembled in 1915, then mass-produced the following year. Machines left port under great secrecy; word was passed that the strange new devices were water tanks for British troops in Egypt. The name "tanks" stuck.

When the terrifying tanks first crawled out on the Western Front, the German government frantically hailed Steiner and one of his tractors to Berlin to begin a race against time. The Hungarian was assigned engineers, draftsmen, supplies. Early in 1917, the group turned out a 14½-foot crawler chassis copied after Holt design. After the addition of heavy armor and guns, this machine—the A7V—was tested and pronounced successful. War lords laid elaborate plans for construction of 2,000 tanks. But time ticked by and disappeared forever as manufacturing facilities were sought among over-taxed and under-manned German plants. German morale and industry sagged exhaustedly to defeat.

The heavy French Saint Chamond, carrying a 75 mm. cannon and machine guns.

French Schneider Tank. Both the Schneider and Saint Chamond retained a tractor-like appearance.

Holt self-propelled gun mount. The machine had a top speed of 30 mph.

. from the track-type tractor evolves a powerful weapon

First Lord of the Admiralty Winston Churchill. He foresaw the need for the formidable tank.

Benjamin Holt and British General Ernest D. Swinton, usually credited with originating the tank . . . at Holt's Stockton plant, April 22, 1918. The miniature at the left was specially constructed for the occasion.

British Mark IV Tank in Peoria . . . presented "in appreciation of the great service rendered Great Britain by The Holt Manufacturing Company during the war."

Caterpillar "75" Tractor and howitzer on the Western Front.

Work Horse for the Army

World War I dawned on a civilization supplied with bigger guns, bigger field pieces than ever before. But the science of off-road mobility—still centered about the horse—was yet in its infancy. Horses and forage claimed too much shipping space, too much care, too much room on the road. They lacked speed and endurance. They were subject to disease and disabling; a sick or dead horse was a menace to an army on the march. Unless rigidly trained, they were quickly frightened by the clang and clamor of war.

The crawler tractor was the answer. For all practical purposes, the Holt company devoted its entire production to the unending needs of the Allies—even well before the U.S. entered the battle. The decision im-

parted immeasurable benefit to the conduct of the war . . . the familiar Caterpillar trademark was welcomed in the Italian Alps, on the Piave, in Gallipoli, Suez, Mesopotamia, Palestine, East Africa, the Western Front —wherever British, French and later American troops traveled—but it left the Holt domestic sales program in a shambles by the time the guns quieted.

Thousands of track-type tractors were shipped from Peoria as the "big three" Allied powers virtually standardized on the Holt-built machines. Hauling heavy artillery and supplies across shell-pocked roads and rain-soaked fields, the crawler became as much a symbol of Allied determination and power as the tractor-bulldozer in World War II.

26

One of 30 track-type units of the Ninth Field Artillery, Honolulu, 1916.
The Ninth became the world's first completely motorized artillery regiment.

General Pershing (left) observing crawler tests, Mexican border, 1916. The Pershing expedition, pursuing Pancho Villa (with troops, right) underlined the need for better roads; machines were expressed from Peoria to tackle the job.

Track-type tractors replaced pack trains hauling supplies to U.S. troop stations along the Rio Grande border, 1917.

THE CHANGING TWENTIES

. . . merger, motor grader,
the tracks that put the world on wheels

After World War I, Best and Holt were again keenly competitive. During the war, both Holt plants had mushroomed almost recklessly to answer Allied tractor needs. Peace found the firm with only the bare nucleus of a sales organization, huge inventories of parts for military tractors and other complexities caused by cancelled war contracts. Wrote Peoria's sales manager: "The Caterpillar crawler Tractor has ceased to be an active factor in the tractor field, both in domestic and foreign markets, excepting in the territory served by Stockton."

C. L. Best Tractor Co., on the other hand, was better equipped for the return to normalcy. From a nucleus of 15 Pacific Coast dealers in 1919, the Best sales roster lengthened to 50 in 1924, including seven export outlets. In the same half-decade, Best sales soared 70%; this in a time when tractor makers' mortality rate stood at an all-time zenith. Principal reason for all this was Best's Sixty Tractor—unveiled in 1919—first to bear the Caterpillar Tractor Co. label six years later and most widely known crawler of the decade.

Holt apprehensions appeared in the 1924 Peoria sales report: "They (Best) are energetically and persistently working all parts of the territory, so they are in touch with practically every prospect that we can obtain, and they are accordingly very active competi-

tion . . . I thoroughly believe that 1925 (will be) a most critical year. If the Best company makes as much progress in the next 12 months as it has in the past year or two, our volume . . . will be menaced . . ." Though its plant facilities were six times and its sales twice as large, the giant of Stockton and Peoria was painfully aware of the gains of its smaller San Leandro rival.

Harry H. Fair of San Francisco was prime mover in the 1925 merger of Best and Holt interests. Use of the widely known Holt trademark "Caterpillar" in the name of the new enterprise was welcomed by both. Best had the better financial status, probably the more advanced tractor design, the beginnings of a better dealer group. Holt offered a world-wide reputation and name, bigger factories and a combined harvester line of 40 years' standing.

Officials of the new corporation adopted the Best Sixty and Thirty and the Holt 2-Ton, 5-Ton and 10-Ton as prime products. The latter two were soon dropped. Prices for 1925 were advertised: Sixty—$6,050; Thirty—$3,665; 2-Ton—$1,975. By the end of 1929, the Sixty's price had fallen five times to $4,300; the Thirty, six times to $2,475. Sales rocketed from $21 million in 1926 to $52 million in 1929. Profits rode along from $4.3 to $12.4 million.

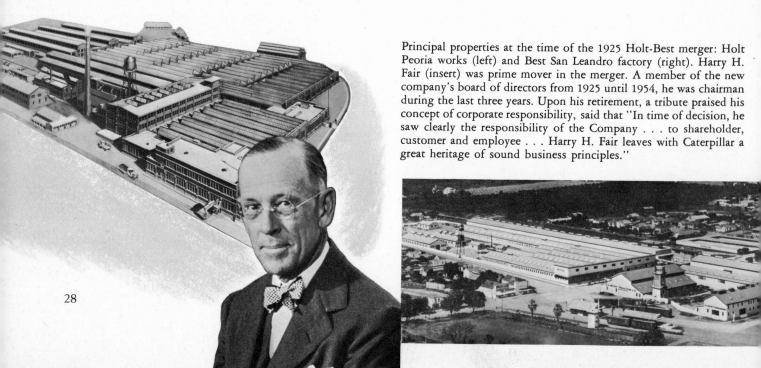

Principal properties at the time of the 1925 Holt-Best merger: Holt Peoria works (left) and Best San Leandro factory (right). Harry H. Fair (insert) was prime mover in the merger. A member of the new company's board of directors from 1925 until 1954, he was chairman during the last three years. Upon his retirement, a tribute praised his concept of corporate responsibility, said that "In time of decision, he saw clearly the responsibility of the Company . . . to shareholder, customer and employee . . . Harry H. Fair leaves with Caterpillar a great heritage of sound business principles."

Above: Engineers who built C. L. Best's famous Sixty Tractor in 1919 scarcely dreamed it would carry the "Caterpillar" trademark six years later. Caterpillar continued the Sixty until 1931.

Right: Holt 10-Ton Tractor near Soldier Field, Chicago, 1924.

Below, right: Caterpillar Thirty Tractor pulling eight-foot grader, 1928. Like the Sixty, the Thirty was originally of Best design and first appeared in 1921. Production stopped in 1932.

Below: Luther Burbank, American naturalist and namesake of the Burbank potato, at the controls of Holt 2-Ton Tractor, 1924.

New Roads . . .
New Machines

By 1830, there were about 27,000 miles of surfaced roads in the U. S.—mainly urban but including a respectable number of turnpikes and rural roads. With the beginning of the railroads' fabulous 70-year boom, the road stopped short and tumbled back into its original role of providing short distance access between carrier (railroad or waterway) and consumer.

Even by 1900, few surfaced roads got beyond city limits. Only seven states had aid programs to promote or coordinate road construction. American roadbuilders floundered along in a desperate effort to keep pace with soaring auto sales. Henry Ford hit a daily production of 1,000 Model Ts in 1913. And the First World War cut quickly into those roadbuilding plans that were on the books.

Afterwards, the U. S. gave its track-type tractors (almost all Caterpillar) to the Bureau of Public Roads for distribution to state highway departments. Thousands of men returned home, having seen the tractor overseas for the first time as a builder. With the horse shortage on the home front, those that stayed home had increased opportunity to see the same thing. At the end of 1918, one California contractor figured up his earnings for the preceding five years: Including contracts for rock and dirt hauling—also plowing, harrowing and harvesting—his Caterpillar "75" Tractor had grossed over $111,000 . . . with the machine still far from worn out.

The mechanization of roadbuilding and the Federal Highway Act of 1921 together sounded the real rise of U. S. roadbuilding. The Act authorized more than $1 billion in federal funds for the dozen years following and motivated appropriation of state monies for the same purpose. Most important, it got states to designate principal interstate and intercounty routes, and tied together their rambling road systems.

Most of today's two-lane highways were born then. The boom's momentum carried through into the thirties when one state after another fizzled out. But the given objective of a two-lane system connecting primary population centers was a reality. Motor vehicle registrations had tripled to about 27 million . . . to remain virtually unchanged until the end of the Second World War. And as the twenties unfolded, new equipment appeared in front, in back and on top of the crawler—bigger scrapers, bulldozers and other tools. Result—cost of moving highway dirt dropped steadily.

Building a new street in suburban St. Paul, 1890. Even with low wages, inexpensive tools and a relatively deflated dollar, highway earthmoving costs were about 25% higher than now.

America's first cross-country motor truck trip, 1911. These gasoline pioneers frequently had to build as they traveled.

Automobile production was far ahead of the road—as it is today. The Model T made its bow in 1908. By 1927, over 15 million of Ford's famous cars had rolled off his lines.

The Holt-built Caterpillar Land Leveler served as a scraper on road jobs like this one—with Holt 5-Ton Tractor, 1920.

Roadbuilding in the twenties often took on a military aspect—typified by this armored 10-Ton Tractor—one of thousands presented by the U.S. to state highway departments after World War I.

Excavating along a new highway site, 1925. Builders turned out bigger wagons to match increasing crawler power.

Fastest dirt digger of the twenties—the elevating grader.

From the road plow evolved the ripper, a deep digging tool useful in preparing new road sites and repairing old ones.

Roadbuilding with Holt 2-Ton Tractor and Fresno scraper, 1922. The five horses in background pulled an identical rig.

A big step forward from the Fresno and rollover scrapers, these multiple units more fully utilized the crawler's digging and hauling capacity. Each was separately controlled.

Caterpillar Twenty Tractor with bulldozer, 1930. The bulldozer grew into the constructor's jack-of-all-trades . . . not only for building roads but also for keeping them clear when winter arrived.

Still another milepost in scraper development, this model gave operator control of the scraper bowl. For the first time, the tractor-scraper became a one-man combination.

One of the many new excavating tools developed by equipment manufacturers was the front-end shovel. This 1932 model was mounted on a Caterpillar Fifteen Tractor.

33

Evolution of the Roadbuilder

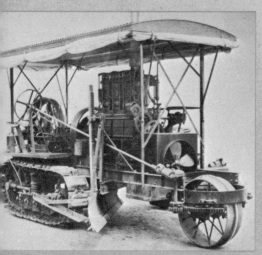

The moldboard suspended under this Holt 1910 model is one example of early efforts to combine both power source and grader blade into one machine.

Russell Motor Patrol, 1919 . . . engineered from a farm tractor power unit and a lightweight highway maintainer.

Early Caterpillar self-propelled graders were track-type tractor mounted . . . as was this Ten Motor Patrol, 1929.

Cruising along dams, levees and highways, the motor grader is a familiar sight . . . six-wheeled, cutting, casting and mixing . . . its two front wheels leaning, and the entire machine at times looking as if it were about to topple into the ditch. Sometimes 25 feet long, the motor grader is one of the more versatile devices in the builder's bag of tools. It cuts out roads and cares for them; blades and lays surfacing materials; removes snow; levels and drains large building sites and airports; throws up farm terraces; fills gullies; builds ditches and shoulders; backfills and grades pipeline paths . . . works backward as well as forward and shapes and shaves grades anywhere from horizontal to straight up.

Before World War I, graders were characteristically lightweight and horse-drawn. Heavier machines weighing up to 8,000 pounds came gradually into use. Later, the crawler shouldered the job of pulling these larger graders; for more than a decade, this was one of its primary uses.

The first self-propelled graders, with blade and power unit incorporated into one machine, appeared just prior to 1920. For a number of years, they were simply grader frames mounted on wheel or crawler tractors—

their use limited to surface maintenance. But, as traffic and road construction boomed, these new tools grew in weight and power—and popularity.

Caterpillar entered the road machinery business in 1928 when it acquired the widely known Russell Grader Manufacturing Company of Minneapolis. Three years later, acknowledging the need for a more versatile, more powerful self-propelled grader, Caterpillar introduced its auto patrol—design predecessor of all current makes of motor grader. Even then, tractor-drawn graders continued to handle heavy jobs such as ditching and grading. Auto patrols stuck to surface work like blading asphalt, finishing subgrades and scarifying and maintaining existing roads.

Construction men came to lean increasingly on the auto patrol—creating demand for an even heavier machine equal to the entire grading job. With the addition of low pressure tires, oscillating tandem drive, diesel power, leaning front wheels, a strong single section frame and a greater range of blade positions, the auto patrol of 1931 became the motor grader of 1938 —a full-fledged construction tool. Because of the motor grader, Caterpillar soon discontinued its line of terracers and blade and elevating graders.

In 1931, Caterpillar engineers introduced the revolutionary auto patrol—with convenient power controls and engine up back of the operator.

The heavier, more versatile Caterpillar Motor Grader made its bow in 1938, and soon displaced both the auto patrol and the pull grader.

More Holt Harvesters

Holt Model 38 Harvester combining wheat on a 60-degree Washington slope.

Soon after formation of Caterpillar Tractor Co. in 1925, six city blocks of Holt facilities in Stockton became a subsidiary, the Western Harvester Company. Purpose— continue the 40-year line of Holt combined harvesters under the Holt name. Salesmen ticked off possible savings over the combine's long standing competitor — the binder-thresher method: lower operating costs . . . savings in grain . . . cleaner land and cleaner grain . . . easier fall plowing. True, salesmen said, certain grains will fall or shatter if left standing until fully ripe. Or grain ripening might be particularly uneven. Or weed growth might be excessive. In that case, use the windrow method. Here, grain is cut early and laid down in the stubble with a windrow header attachment. Two to six days later, grain is picked up with another attachment; then put through the combine. Still no binding and threshing crews necessary—only two men for dinner!

Windrow pick-up unit with Model 34 Combine. When harvester manufacture moved to a new Peoria factory in 1930, machines began wearing the Caterpillar trademark. The combine line was discontinued in 1935.

1930—Oregon Governor A. W. Norblad shuts off the gas. Colorful ceremonies marked the end of a world's record 481-hour run conducted by Oregon State College.

Farm
Tractor Market

"If you want to make farm sales, hunt!" the Company urged dealer salesmen. "Hunt for prospects . . . hunt for facts . . . then if you're stuck, hunt us up. Open gates . . . ring doorbells . . . sit on water troughs and fences . . . wear out some chalk on the back of the tool shed!" So Caterpillar promoted farm use of crawler power, particularly the Ten, Fifteen and Twenty. Home office publications recommended use of new farm tools of the twenties; showed crawlers plowing, planting and harvesting . . . in beans, beets, grains, fruits, rice, truck crops . . . hauling wagons, leveling land, building roads and ditches, dusting, spraying, clearing . . . pulling harrows, subsoilers, drills, planters, binders, mowers, loaders, corn pickers, potato diggers, combines. More traction, less slippage, less soil packing, more work done—better, quicker, cheaper. This was the theme.

New pick-up baler and Caterpillar Ten Tractor, 1930.

Caterpillar Fifteen Tractor and two-row corn picker.

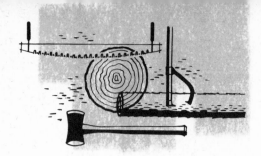

First in the Forests

Out of the woods in the twenties came a new dialect for Caterpillar salesmen—thanks to the customers who first showed the way. Salesmen learned that trees in a timber stand were scaled in M.b.f.—thousands of board-feet. Where a logging show was a good tractor chance, logs were cut, bunched and chokers attached. Yarding down to the landing might be accomplished by ground or pan skidding . . . by bummer hauling . . . by high-wheel or drum-wheel logging. The crew might include choker setters, swampers, landing men, fallers and buckers. On harder shows, crawler tractors might turn donkey and cold-deck logs. Crawlers were also useful, the customer counseled, in swamping new shows, chunking out trails, building mudsill bridges, feeding logs on a donkey chance, trailing log chutes, salvaging sinker logs, moving cabins, constructing fire breaks and hauling sleighs over the snow.

Oil is Where You Find It

In the twenties, drillers found oil far out from good roads in broken country, swamps, deserts and even under water. When a tractor salesman ventured from farm to forest to oilfield, he discovered still another language . . . and new applications for his versatile product. Here, a log was a geological record rather than the wherewithal for a new house. Here, the farm boss cared little about crops but knew plenty about the lease labor and equipment he managed. Here, spuds were drilling tools, not potatoes. Here, roustabouts were skilled laborers and gang pushers and roughnecks also part of job terminology. Track-type tractors and their rear-mounted winches skidded boilers and bull wheels into place . . . drilled and serviced wells . . . built roads around proven leases . . . leveled and maintained tank farms. For one of the world's toughest tasks—pipelining—crawlers cleared the right-of-way, strung and laid pipe, then backfilled over it.

THE PHILIPPINES . . . Plowing swampy rice fields, 1931.

INDIA . . . Twenty Tractor and blade grader, 1930.

SCOTLAND . . . 1932—Farming with Caterpillar Ten Tractor.

gasoline gives way to a better power idea...

Wearing only the matter-of-fact serial 1C1, the first Caterpillar Diesel Tractor went to work in 1931. In 1933, the Company's production of diesel horsepower exceeded that of the entire U.S. for the preceding year. When the nation's diesel production hit two million horsepower in 1937, Caterpillar accounted for one-third of the total. The track-type tractor had become the largest user of diesel power; the Company, the largest manufacturer.

By the end of 1933, customers had signed for over 2,000 diesel crawlers. Even in the throes of depression, sales reflected the market impact of the new power idea. From $24 million in 1931 and $13 million the following year, sales rose to $54 and $63 million in 1936 and 1937. Employment hit 11,500 at the close of 1936—4,000 over the 1929 pre-depression peak and 8,000 over the 1931 figure. In Peoria, at least, times were good.

The far-reaching impact of the first diesel crawlers was an impressive demonstration of the value of research—being first with a new and sound idea. The diesel engine itself, however, was hardly a new concept. The first American version appeared in 1898. Even then, its ability to use cheaper fuels than could be burned by gasoline engines—to provide superior operating characteristics at higher efficiency—was well known.

The great problem lay in borrowing the diesel idea from its primary use—heavy stationary and marine installations—and adapting it to tractor application. Easier said than done. Stationary diesels were bulky and expensive. Compactness and field maintenance were no problems. Units usually operated at uniform speed under uniform load. On the other hand, the tractor diesel meant higher speeds ... new fuel and lubricating oil filtering problems ... stronger, lighter metals with better ability to conduct and resist heat.

After testing a number of diesel engines, many of them foreign-built, Caterpillar engineers determined to put together an entirely new engine. The unit was to operate smoothly and efficiently under a wide variety of loads. It was to be free from delicate checks and adjustments. It was to incorporate its own independent starting system, be easy to service and operate, have dustproof operating parts. Model 1C1 reached its first owner only after two years of designing and testing. It led the U.S. into the fabulous diesel upsurge of the thirties and forties. It pioneered the way for an industry that today runs almost 100% on diesel fuel.

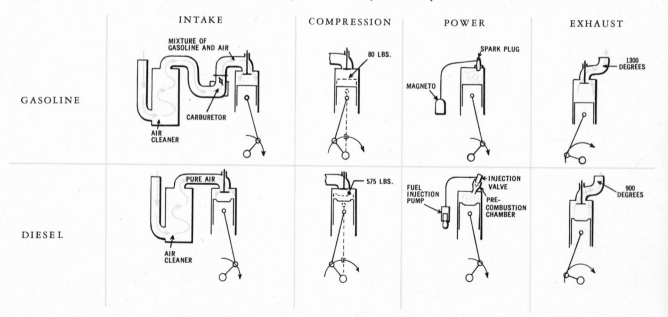

The Company compared gasoline and diesel cycles. Basic difference is that diesel has no carburetor or electrical system; combustion occurs with injection of fuel into compressed air.

Caterpillar Diesel Tractor and rubber-tired scraper carving Treasure Island approach to the San Francisco Bay Bridge, 1938.

Signs of the times . . . Bowery breadline, 1930.

Signs of the times . . . Parched soil drifting like snow, 1934.

Selling the Diesel

The vaunted American flair for salesmanship—claimed as key to the halcyon twenties—seemed to be crowding the wailing wall along with everything else in the early thirties. Had the desires of millions for better food, better clothing, better homes . . . had all these things disappeared with the disappointing ticker tape of a few years back? Were consumers really broke? Could the tractor salesman still sell tractors . . . and diesel tractors at that?

Yes, said Alexander Botts, William Hazlett Upson's whimsical promoter who always closed the sale with a happy ending. Yes, said Caterpillar salesmen. The new engine provides better operating characteristics; example—three to four times the torque response during an overload. Yes . . . because the diesel uses lower cost fuel—generally priced at less than half its gasoline competition. Yes . . . because the diesel gets more out of each gallon of fuel.

Dealers were urged to consider first diesel sales in their territories as a vital seed crop. Early buyers should be men of influence—situated where the dealer's service department could keep daily check on the new machines. The diesel meant new selling methods and efforts; new service and field problems. Huge trucks left the factory to take part in one-day dealer schools all over the country. Diesel shows and schools played to tens of thousands of customers, prospects and anyone else who cared to sit in. Demonstrations highlighted the diesel's ability to burn a wide variety of cheap fuels. On one such demonstration, freshly harvested soy beans were crushed in a hand driven press and the resulting vegetable oil poured into a tractor's fuel tank. It ran.

Such free-swinging promotions were not without pitfalls. By the time the Company's claims concerning wide diesel fuel appetites were embellished by salesmen, customers sometimes let imagination outrun logic and fed machines anything and everything. When an Arkansas diesel tractor fleet, for example, showed incredible fuel pump damage, researchers discovered the owner was getting phenomenal fuel economy—by dumping used crankcase oil into his tanks!

Impact of the diesel idea soon appeared in the remainder of the Caterpillar line. New models: the Seventy-Five, Fifty and Thirty-Five in 1933 . . . the Forty in 1934 . . . the RD8, RD7 and RD6 in 1935 . . . the RD4 in 1936 and the D2 in 1938. Successor to the 2-Ton, Twenty and Twenty-Two, the D2 made its bow at a lower price than that of the smaller, less powerful gasoline 2-Ton in 1925. In 1934, five newly dieselized auto patrols left Peoria to cover 30,000 miles and 200 demonstrations in all 48 states.

Signs of the times . . . WPA moves earth the old way, 1935.

Crowd around diesel crawler at close of world's record run, April 29, 1932. Going 23 hours daily, six days a week, the machine had plowed 6,880 acres of Oregon soil in 46 days. Costs for fuel, lube oils, grease and repairs totaled only 7.78¢ per acre—a startling demonstration of low-cost dieselized farming. Commented the *Oregon Farmer:* "As the group of 150 men from half a dozen states watched . . . in the closing hours of one of the most spectacular performances in the history of big-scale farming, some of them had the thought in mind that they were present at an historic event . . . a distinctive milepost in the long trail of agricultural history."

From the pages of the *Saturday Evening Post*, Alexander Botts came to life. Joe E. Brown dramatized exploits of the irrepressible Botts in a 1936 movie, "Earthworm Tractors."

Opening the second section of the Albert Canal, 1934. Early in 1932, 10 of the first 25 Caterpillar Diesel Tractors went to Belgium to move almost two million yards of earth here.

Caterpillar equipment users since 1913, Schuder Bros. of Woodland, California, bought the second diesel crawler in 1931. Nine years and 16,000 operating hours later, the owner tallied his total fuel savings over gasoline power—$9.120.

Diesel Seventy-Five and Hyster Arch make short work of 600-year-old log. The Seventy-Five appeared in 1933.

Diesel Forty gets Pan American clipper out of the water.

Hauling on a road contract near Washington, D.C., 1936. Diesel RD8 was of 1935 vintage.

Along the original Pennsylvania Turnpike, 1940. Contractors' big diesel powered fleets moved 26 million cubic yards of earth here to begin a new American roadbuilding era.

This 1938 model Diesel D2 replaced a smaller gasoline tractor and operated on one-fourth the fuel bill.

45

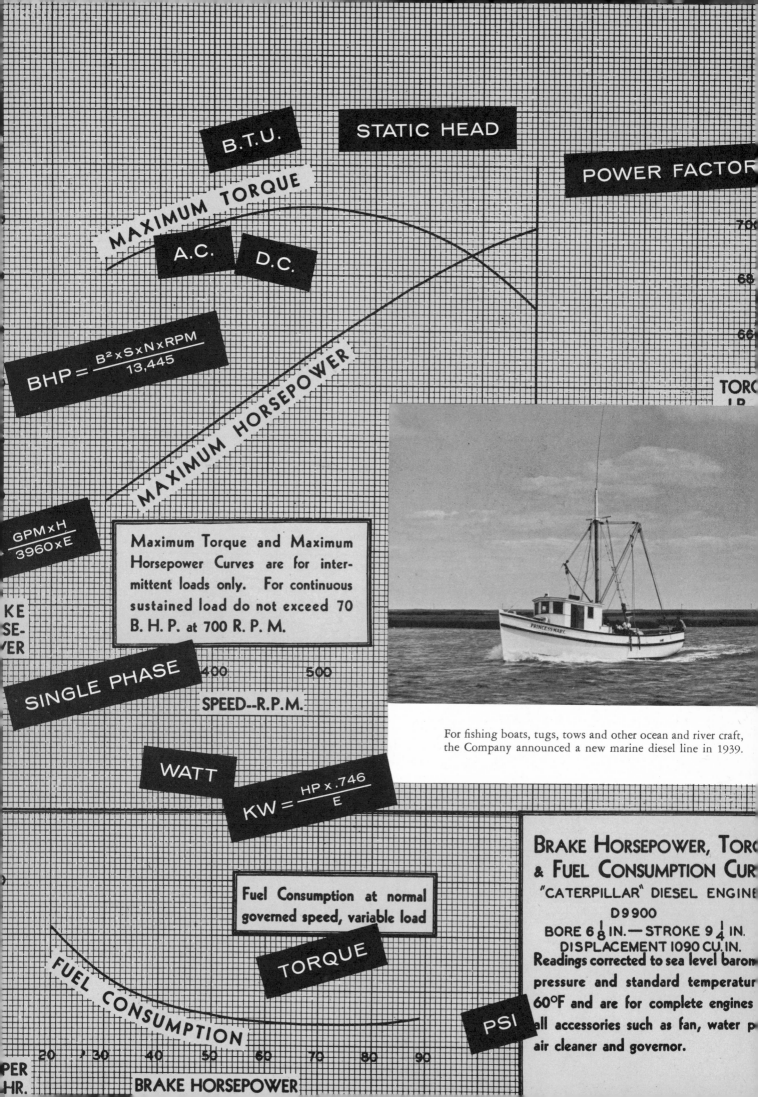

B.T.U.

STATIC HEAD

POWER FACTOR

MAXIMUM TORQUE

A.C.   D.C.

$$BHP = \frac{B^2 \times S \times N \times RPM}{13,445}$$

MAXIMUM HORSEPOWER

700

68

66

TORC
LB

$$\frac{GPM \times H}{3960 \times E}$$

Maximum Torque and Maximum Horsepower Curves are for intermittent loads only. For continuous sustained load do not exceed 70 B. H. P. at 700 R. P. M.

KE
SE-
VER

SINGLE PHASE

400   500

SPEED--R.P.M.

WATT

$$KW = \frac{HP \times .746}{E}$$

For fishing boats, tugs, tows and other ocean and river craft, the Company announced a new marine diesel line in 1939.

Fuel Consumption at normal governed speed, variable load

TORQUE

FUEL CONSUMPTION

PSI

BRAKE HORSEPOWER, TORC
& FUEL CONSUMPTION CUR
"CATERPILLAR" DIESEL ENGINE
D 9900
BORE 6 $\frac{1}{8}$ IN. — STROKE 9 $\frac{1}{4}$ IN.
DISPLACEMENT 1090 CU. IN.
Readings corrected to sea level barom
pressure and standard temperatur
60°F and are for complete engines
all accessories such as fan, water p
air cleaner and governor.

20   30   40   50   60   70   80   90

PER
HR.

BRAKE HORSEPOWER

The Engine Business

When a crawler had worked out a lifetime of usefulness, owners often unbolted the engine and put it to work pumping water, running a sawmill or perhaps generating electricity in a small industrial plant. Recognizing this demand potential, Caterpillar organized a special division in 1931 to seek stationary and portable markets for its five gasoline engines.

The engine business, however, really got started with introduction of the new diesel units. To many users, news of diesel economies meant even more than it did to tractor buyers. Reason: Two thousand hours was a good year's schedule for a tractor; fuel expense rarely ran as high, for example, as yearly depreciation on the over-all machine. On a water pumping or municipal power installation, on the other hand, engines often operated around the clock, seven days a week . . . piling up three and even four times as many hours. Fuel represented the largest single expense; fuel saving possibilities were huge.

The first Caterpillar Diesel Engine went to an excavator manufacturer. Makers of excavators, compressors, gravel plants, drill rigs, locomotives and similar equipment quickly acknowledged the attractiveness of offering diesel power with their machines. From nine such customers in 1932, the list rose to 17 in 1933, doubled to 34 in 1934 and went over the 100 mark in 1938. Here again, the customer showed the way . . . recommending special accessories and adaptations to better fit the diesel for non-tractor work.

Engine sales to manufacturers increased dealer parts and service business. And the world-wide Caterpillar dealer organization, in turn, strengthened manufacturer sales opportunities . . . because it comprised a ready-made service source . . . and because long-standing customers welcomed the chance to standardize on one engine make.

The engine business broadened sales outlets to existing customers—the contractor in need of new engines for old compressors, crushers, conveyors, excavators, generators . . . the logger to be contacted about sawmill power. And there were new customers as well: cotton ginners, flour and feed millers, ice plant and hatchery owners—anyone whose power costs could be lowered with diesel. To his bag of definitions, the salesman added I equals E over R; rolling resistance and cycle time made room for British Thermal Units and kilowatt-hours.

A number of manufacturers—such as this one—advertised use of the new Caterpillar Diesel Engines in their products.

Caterpillar D7700 Diesel pumps 1,150 gallons per minute to irrigate 260 Colorado acres, 1936. Hourly fuel cost—26¢.

WORLD WAR II

.... for the fortunes of war,

conversion and reconversion

Pipelaying became vital as submarines sank tankers off the Eastern Seaboard faster than they were being built.

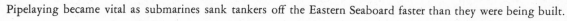

When war came to the U.S. in December, 1941, the idea that Caterpillar products and factories would be drafted for duty was hardly news to Company people. Almost all 1941 sales had already gone for defense uses. And of the 30% of 1940 production channeled overseas, the bulk had been delivered to the Allies for military construction.

Five months before Pearl Harbor, the Ordnance Department asked Caterpillar to come up with a radial air-cooled diesel for its M4 Tank. Pulling all stops, engineers set a completed model on the test block in January, 1942. A month later, the new Caterpillar Military Engine Company began construction of a Decatur, Illinois, plant for manufacture of the tank diesels. In July, 1943, the first engine rolled off the line. Field tests proved its workability: The dieselized tank could use heavy black oils and low octane gasolines as well as conventional fuel . . . and its superior torque reserve was an important advantage in hilly country.

In Peoria, workmen turned out transmissions and final drive assemblies for the same tank. In addition, Caterpillar produced 155 mm. howitzer carriages, shells, bomb parts and track-type mechanisms for military vehicles. Garbed in their familiar highway yellow, standard Caterpillar products were much in demand . . . not only for stepped-up standard work such as logging, farming and stripping out new coal seams . . . but also for "crash" projects: laying pipelines, building war plants, constructing armed forces training centers.

Completed in November, 1942, the Alcan Highway was called the "Road to Tokyo," the greatest construction project since the Panama Canal. Winding 1,600 miles from Dawson Creek to Fairbanks, it crashed through timber, hacked across mountains and floated over muskeg swamps. Of the hundreds of crawlers on the job, the great majority were Peoria-built.

Milling aluminum cylinder heads for diesel tank engine, 1943. Women made up 30% of the wartime work force.

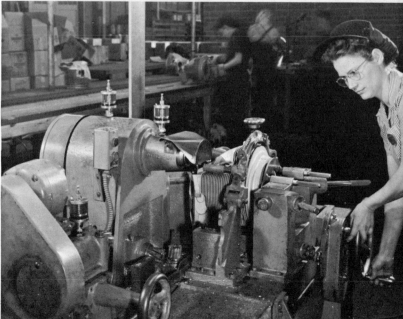

A Bucket of Olive Drab

Said one military official: "If large stores of tractors and tanks waited on a wharf for shipment to an enemy combat zone, and but one transport were available, we would frequently choose the tractors." As the complexion of the war became clearer, crawler tractors scored higher and higher on the country's most wanted list.

This was truest in the Pacific. The South Pacific became one gigantic airstrip with the advent of "island hopping." You landed men and machines . . . moved them inland . . . built bases and airstrips . . . then got ready to take on the next island-outpost. Battle meant fast movement on the ground and intensive action in the sky—with roads and airstrips the key to both. Heavy construction equipment pushed into the pages of every battle plan.

All this meant reconversion for Caterpillar—but in 1943, with the war hardly half won. No more tank diesels and other special production . . . only tractors, motor graders, engines and electric sets from here on in. And equipping standard machines for wartime tasks was easy. A liberal dousing of G.I. olive drab paint was about all that was needed.

Photographic records of the Company's track-type tractors and motor graders look like journals of World War II. Names like Guadalcanal, Tarawa, Attu, Anzio, Kwajalein, Eniwetok, Saipan, Tinian, Guam, Normandy, the Philippines, Iwo Jima, Okinawa. Tractors went in with the second wave of amphibious troops . . . down ramps and through the surf with Seabees and Army Engineers . . . dragging steel mats or supplies, bulldozer blades up for protection . . . then blades down, building temporary roads on higher ground, throwing up earthworks, pushing off stranded landing craft, preparing the beach for the next wave of troops.

"Boss of the Beach," said Army Engineers chief Major General Eugene Reybold about the tractor-bulldozer. "The indispensable, all-purpose weapon of the Engineers." Tractors built airstrips, military roads, camps, munitions "igloos," trenches and tank traps . . . hauled guns and supplies, towed aircraft, filled bomb craters, cleared debris, routed out enemy pillboxes . . . positioned pontoon bridges, prepared river and stream banks for crossing and bridging. Portable engines and electric sets cranked out light and power for advance bases and bombed-out locales.

Back home, Caterpillar was as hard pressed as its products overseas. Means had to be found to push employment up from 11,000 at the beginning of 1940 to 20,000 at the end of 1944—this with high turnover, a relatively small labor market and 6,000 employees off to the armed forces. Engineers and metallurgists had to make-do with substitute materials and yet not endanger the Company's long standing quality record. And with 85% of output going directly to the government, dealers had to find new conservation techniques to stay in business and keep customers moving earth.

General Joseph W. Stilwell checks progress on his Burma-Ledo Road, 1944. Snaking 620 miles across monsoon-swollen rivers and fever-infested jungles, the war-built artery opened the way for China convoys.

NEW GEORGIA

LONDON

ATTU

LEYTE

ITALY

NEW GUINEA

NORTH AFRICA

"The four machines that won the war in the Pacific were the submarine, radar, the airplane and the tractor—bulldozer"

—Admiral William F. Halsey

NEW PRODUCTS
FOR AN OLD SCIENCE

. . . for the earthmoving business,
yellow paint and new nameplates

Without its collection of tools and trappings, a horse is transportation and not much more. The same for a tractor. A mobile power plant, it specializes in an unchanging sort of muscle power; all of its varied work is accomplished by an assortment of engaging tools which are pushed ahead . . . or pulled behind . . . or mounted upon the machine. Such devices are required for every tractor operation.

The Caterpillar line of 1925 included just five machines—all crawler tractors. Excepting terracers and blade and elevating graders, Caterpillar did not quantity-manufacture any engaging tools until after the Second World War. Through the twenties and thirties and war, such auxiliary products had been engineered and fabricated by a fast-growing group of

equipment manufacturers . . . then sold through the dealer organization. Prior to 1936, over 80 such products had been listed in Company literature . . . including bulldozers made by 11 different firms and 20 brands of scrapers.

After this date, the list of auxiliary manufacturers shortened. Many began tailoring their products more specifically to one tractor make . . . which gave them new flexibility and broader research opportunities. And, as the years passed, Caterpillar started marketing a number of these items. In 1944, for example, the Company announced its intention to build a line of matched earthmoving equipment that now includes scrapers, wagons, rippers, bulldozers, tractor shovels, tool bars and cable and hydraulic controls.

First (1940) Caterpillar rubber-tired tractor model and matching wagon—early evidence of the Company's entry into the field of more specialized earthmoving equipment.

The ripper is an oversize plow for pulling up pavement or penetrating as deep as 2½ feet into rock and packed or frozen ground. Caterpillar makes rippers in two sizes.

Bulldozers come in straight, angling and "U" shapes—both cable and
hydraulically controlled. First Caterpillar Bulldozer left Peoria in 1945.

Old and New Wonders

With its sales force already skilled in the application of earthmoving machinery, Caterpillar was hardly a fledgling in the field. Likewise, the business of moving earth was nothing new under the sun. Early construction projects stack up against today's largest. Example: The Pyramid of Cheops, displacing a volume greater than all but the largest of modern dams. Or the Great Wall of China—meandering 1,400 miles through mountains and valleys—and bulwarked with 72 million cubic yards of earth . . . or almost three times the yardage handled on the original Pennsylvania Turnpike.

With a comparison of the size of ancient and modern projects, the similarity ends. Today's builder is doing the job much better, much quicker and much cheaper.

The scraper's evolution is a case in point. A man with shovel and wheelbarrow could dig and move about three cubic yards of dirt 500 feet in a 12-hour day. With a typical two-horse Fresno drag scraper, circa 1900, he boosted his output about four times. Now take the same drag scraper . . . add wheels and power to raise and lower the scraper bowl . . . add ejector and apron . . . add rubber tires for the wheels . . . build it big enough to gulp up 35 tons of earth in a single pass . . . and you have a modern scraper. So that one man with a diesel crawler out front can do 150 times more work than the man with the Fresno—in the same time over the same haul. And, despite the higher price tag on his tools and time, do so at about 20% less cost than in 1900.

Begun over 5,000 years ago, the Great Pyramid required 30 years and the services of 100,000 slaves to complete.

Thousands of men took 18 years to construct the earth-filled Great Wall of China. The top forms a 13-foot roadway.

With the scraper, one man can dig, haul and spread earth—operations once requiring three separate tools. To dig, operator lowers the scraper bowl so that it cuts into the ground as it moves along. When scraper is loaded, he raises the bowl, shifts gears and speeds off to the fill. Here, he first opens the apron at the machine's front; then brings the ejector forward—fast or slow depending on the spread depth desired. Customers first bought Caterpillar Scrapers in 1946.

The high speed DW21 Tractor (introduced 1950) moves 20 cubic yards of highway dirt at 20 miles per hour.

A Yard of Earth

Earthmoving engineers like to label their profession an art instead of a science . . . because in no other field are the variables quite so variable. Keystone of the entire industry is a measurement of one cubic yard—which is to earthmoving what the No. 303 can is to the soup business. The contractor figures costs and profits on a cubic yard basis. If his estimates are correct and his bid low, he gets the contract. If his bid isn't too low, he makes money.

In-place yards on which the contractor bids and loose yards which he actually hauls are never alike. The cubic yard is a will-o'-the-wisp. It seldom weighs the same and it expands whenever disturbed. A cubic yard of gravel, for example, weighs about 2,700 pounds and swells 10% larger than its original size by the time it rolls inside a scraper. A cubic yard of limestone, on the other hand, will go 4,400 pounds and swell 60%.

If the cubic yard qualifies as firm earth, the crawler tractor working on it can express most of its weight in pounds pull. If the yard is loose sand, however, less than half of tractor weight is available. If the yard is half-way up a mountain, more engine will be needed to move it than at sea level.

When hauling the cubic yard, a tractor overcomes rolling resistance. For this, it expends from 40 to 400 pounds pull per ton, depending on the haul road's condition. And if the yard is to travel uphill, the tractor will need still more pounds of pull. Before the cubic yard is finally priced, the contractor figures in loading and dumping time . . . and time for accelerating, braking, shifting gears. Lastly, he remembers that neither people nor machines work 60-minute hours and corrects for operator fatigue and routine maintenance.

Proper selection of equipment is a vital preamble to cost estimating. For short haul excavation up to two or three hundred feet, crawler-bulldozers are most economical. On longer hauls, where haul roads are not practicable or where conditions are especially challenging, crawler-scrapers generally take over. Beyond is the high speed haul zone. Here, the rubber-tired tractor best uses its principal advantage—speed.

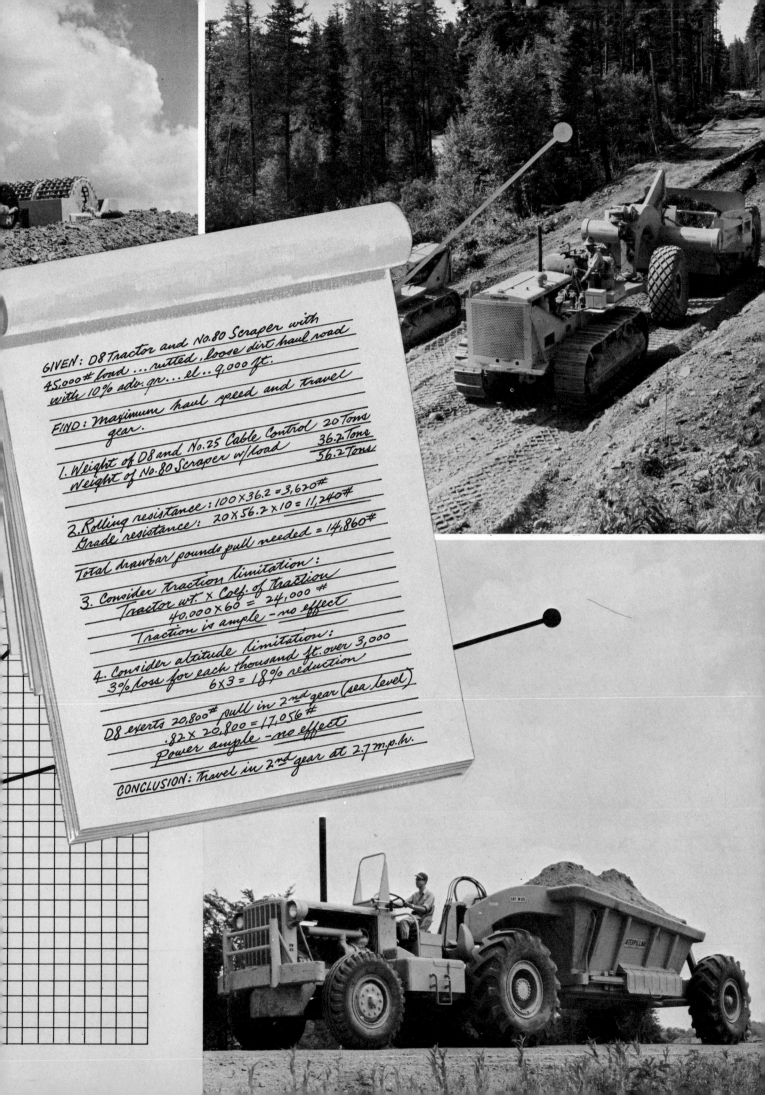

GIVEN: D8 Tractor and No. 80 Scraper with 45,000# load ... rutted, loose dirt haul road with 10% adv. gr... el.. 9,000 ft.

FIND: Maximum haul speed and travel gear.

1. Weight of D8 and No.25 Cable Control   20 Tons
   Weight of No. 80 Scraper w/load   36.2 Tons
                                          56.2 Tons

2. Rolling resistance : $100 \times 36.2 = 3,620\#$
   Grade resistance : $20 \times 56.2 \times 10 = 11,240\#$

   Total drawbar pounds pull needed $= 14,860\#$

3. Consider Traction limitation :
   Tractor wt. × Coef. of Traction
        $40,000 \times 60 = 24,000\#$
   Traction is ample - no effect

4. Consider altitude limitation :
   3% loss for each thousand ft. over 3,000
        $6 \times 3 = 18\%$ reduction

   D8 exerts $20,800\#$ pull in 2nd gear (sea level)
        $.82 \times 20,800 = 17,056\#$
   Power ample - no effect

   CONCLUSION: Travel in 2nd gear at 2.7 m.p.h.

Pennsylvania basement, 1940 ... dug in a half-day on 75¢ worth of diesel fuel by D4 Tractor and Traxcavator Shovel.

Trackson Acquired

In December, 1951, Caterpillar bought the Trackson Company. Organized in 1922, the Milwaukee firm started producing hoists, cranes and other tractor attachments in 1928. Its first (1936) attachment for Caterpillar machines was a pipe layer. The year follow-ing, its High Lift Shovel appeared. The subsidiary now builds a line of pipe layers as well as hydraulically con-trolled tractor shovels for the Company's crawlers.

A tractor shovel is a kind of second story bulldozer. It can bite three tons of earth out of a new basement, spin around and deposit it in a truck or on a bank 10 feet above. It loads logs, lumber, pipe, dirt, coal. It spots railroad cars and landscapes back yards. It strips, stock-piles, grades, removes snow. It picks slag out of open hearth furnaces and grabs ore from underground veins.

Engineers built the new (1953) Traxcavator No. 6 for tractor shovel work. Its integrated design was an industry "first."

The Chief rides again

Only yesterday he was handling earthmoving equipment for a contractor. A veteran of the island-hopping campaign in the Pacific, he was known as a man who could do impossible things with a "Cat" Bulldozer. Now he's back in the Service — Chief Petty Officer Herb Plank, of the Seabees.

That's happening to a lot of men and machines these days. Needed for the national defense, they step out of civilian clothes and into battle dress. "Caterpillar" yellow gives way to olive drab on the big, rugged earthmovers that are the primary tools of Army and Air Force Engineers and of Navy Construction Battalions.

Meanwhile "Caterpillar" equipment has other important jobs to do throughout the land. Full production to back the nation's effort is vitally necessary in these times. And the big yellow machines are working overtime in oil fields, mines and logging operations; on farms and highway projects; in dam and airfield construction—helping to get America's big job done.

CATERPILLAR TRACTOR CO., PEORIA, ILL.

CATERPILLAR
DIESEL ENGINES · TRACTORS
MOTOR GRADERS
EARTHMOVING EQUIPMENT

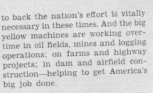

FOR DEFENSE AND FOR PRODUCTION, YOU CAN COUNT ON THE BIG YELLOW MACHINES

Korean War

During four years of intensive post-war building and rearrangement, Caterpillar looked forward to full use of its facilities to meet unfilled customer needs. Most of this period had seen allocation of one sort or another. Then came mid-1950 and Korea and many of the old problems of World War II . . . shortages of critical materials and trained personnel . . . loss of over 1,000 men to the armed forces. But—veterans of far more demanding times and fresh from four years' refurbishing—both plants and people were better equipped to turn quickly to defense needs.

Electromagnet picks up three tons of steel. Foundry uses 4,000 gondolas-full of scrap, pig iron, coke, limestone and sand yearly.

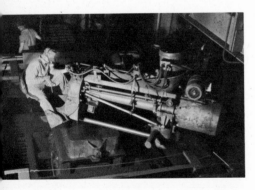

Art Gratz touches up a production pattern for D8 track roller hubs. Molds are made from the finished pattern.

Maneuvered with a joy stick like a Link Trainer, a speed slinger rams sand to brick-like consistency around a D8 engine block pattern.

Foundry Manager Frank Shipley has directed Peoria's 1,600 foundry workers for the last 10 years. A Purdue grad, he joined the Company in 1929.

MAKING OF A D8
...men with machines and materials build 19 tons of tractor

The Caterpillar D8 Tractor weighs 38,155 pounds. It delivers 150 horsepower at the drawbar—which is 55 more than in 1935 when it first appeared. It travels slowly but inexorably at speeds up to 5.8 miles per hour. It plants over 16 feet of broad track surface on the ground and, in spite of its great weight, exerts about as much per-square-inch pressure as that of a man walking.

Like the Company's other crawler models, the D8 is 100% born and raised in its giant Peoria Plant. The latter is 406 acres of ground and 121 acres of buildings in which 21,000 people make a good living (average hourly employee earns about $4,000 yearly). But making of a D8 really begins in the black sand molds of the Peoria foundry. Opened in 1930 to melt 300 tons of iron daily, the foundry now pours up to 600 in the same space. Its sound is the sound of an unending elevated train—punctuated by whistle toots, the sharp hissing of core blowers and the staccato banging of jolting machines.

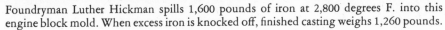

Foundryman Luther Hickman spills 1,600 pounds of iron at 2,800 degrees F. into this engine block mold. When excess iron is knocked off, finished casting weighs 1,260 pounds.

In the comparative hush of the foundry's pattern shop, one of the most skilled of all trades saws and shapes enough mahogany and white pine each year to build six five-room houses. Pattern-making is a precision business that requires a four-year apprenticeship and an equal amount of practice before a man can be considered tops. And it's expensive: one set of production patterns and core boxes for a D8 cylinder head costs $60,000.

The D8 has its genesis in the foundry's four cupolas where 100,000 tons of steaming iron run like rich cream into four million molds yearly. It takes form in light lever arms that go one-half pound apiece . . . or in transmission cases that weigh 3,200 pounds. It takes strength from alloys like nickel and copper and molybdenum. Because air is completely changed two to three times per minute, the foundry stays cleaner and cooler than many other locations in the big Peoria Plant. And for all the clangor and color, it's safer for the men inside than their own homes—according to National Safety Council statistics.

63

Two Lines, 222 Men

Like a huge funnel, the Peoria Plant pours its resources into its assembly lines. Principally for the lines, seven acres of tool cribs dispense everything from hand soap to furnace parts; electrical equipment draws enough electricity to provide light and power for a city of 110,000 homes. To the lines are channeled forgings, castings, weldments, the pieces and parts that are bolted, pressed and set in place.

The Caterpillar D8 Tractor is the product of two lines — one for its engine and another for the tractor itself. First of these is one of three in the Company's new engine factory. At the start of this line are bare engine blocks in three sizes; the largest blocks are used in the D8. Many of all three sizes will never be bolted to a tractor frame. Some are ticketed for air compressors and excavators; others will soon start receiving special equipment and attention to suit them for power assignments in shrimp boats or perhaps engine-generator electric sets.

Eighty men work along the engine line . . . they lower the D8's 336-pound crankshaft to the block and bolt it between seven pairs of aluminum bearings . . . then add pistons, crankcase, cylinder heads and starting engine . . . 142 men work on tractor assembly and add steering clutches, sprockets, fuel tank and floor plates. At the end of the 504-foot tractor line, dozens of machines (two other models in addition to the D8) roll out onto their own tracks each day.

Assemblers Rittgers (left) and McFall guide the D8 down onto pre-assembled track roller frames.

Ruebin Norden (left) spins cap screws into the D8's cylinder heads. Next, he mounts intake and exhaust manifolds and bolts on the fan belt pulley. At right, John Sinks swings the fuel pump assembly into place . . . making sure its drive gear and the timing gear are properly meshed. Lastly, he attaches governor control housing and hooks up governor.

D8 final drive assemblies feed into the tractor line. With a power hoist, Luther Keedy positions the assembly, affixes it with 26 bolts. After performing the same operation on the other side, Keedy picks two final drive pinion bearings out of a "freeze box" (—67 degrees F.). The low temperature shrinks the big bearings, makes them easier to press home.

65

Behind the Lines—Care

A D8 Tractor is a machine of many parts. These are expected to stay whole and stay together in temperatures from 65 below zero to 125 above, through dirt and dust and generally through more abuse than is the lot of any other self-propelled vehicle. Customers expect an operating life of about 20,000 hours (the time equivalent of one million miles' automobile travel); some machines have operated five times that long. Downtime in the tractor business means a good deal more than the price of a part; it can mean a stalemated job schedule and loss of income.

To lengthen the life of its machines, Caterpillar makes a point of precision and mass-produced quality. Its Peoria inspection corps numbers over 950 strong. Its investment in heat treat facilities alone runs well into the millions. For the entire product line, over 7,000 parts—including the D8's 350-pound sprockets —get added strength and hardness by heat treatment. Time of treatment varies from two seconds to 36 hours; one huge furnace is 107 feet long.

Track bushings go down into a carburizing furnace for heat treatment. Ancient as the swords of Damascus, the process hardens bushing surfaces; cores remain soft and tough.

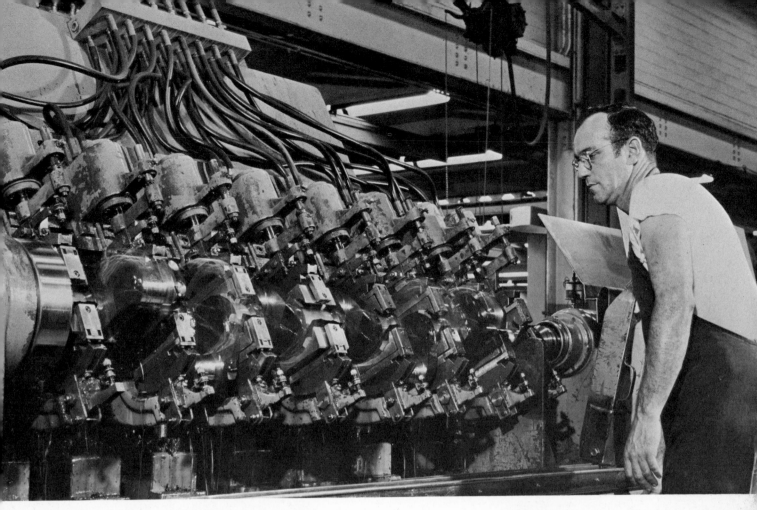

Bill Martindale superfinishes main journals of a D8 crank-shaft—a four-minute operation. With this machine, purchased for $31,000 in 1948, crankshaft journals are polished to within five-millionths of an inch of perfect smoothness.

Precombustion chamber and 2⅞-inch steel stock from which it is made. An automatic screw machine performs eight machining operations, turns out 19 of the pieces hourly.

General Foreman Harold Dingerson compares D8 connecting rods—the smaller for the gasoline starting engine, the larger for the diesel. Machinists must get connecting rod bores within two ten-thousandths of an inch of specified diameter.

67

Rough stores bay in the Company's engine factory is one-fifth mile long.
Parts come in at right, go down machining lines beginning at left.

Completed D8 treadmills on greased
test skids before painting and shipping.

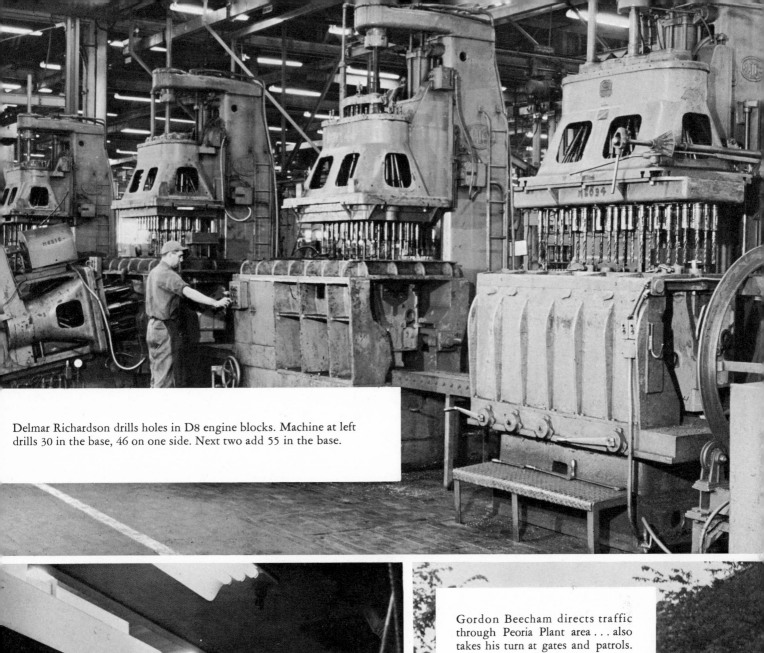

Delmar Richardson drills holes in D8 engine blocks. Machine at left drills 30 in the base, 46 on one side. Next two add 55 in the base.

Trained mechanics like Harvey Troxell check and adjust D8 engines in specially equipped cells.

Gordon Beecham directs traffic through Peoria Plant area . . . also takes his turn at gates and patrols.

Making of the D9

Beginning in the spring of 1954, nine customers saw sneak previews of the D9. They were looking at the world's largest, most powerful tractor. It weighed over 28 tons, measured approximately 18 feet long, 10 feet wide, nine feet high. Engineers claimed it would usher in a new era of crawler productivity.

From coast to coast, the previews unfolded on customers' jobs. One of the machines turned logger in Washington State. One wound up hitched to a giant scraper. Another went to work along the Ohio Turnpike . . . another on a new dam . . . still another on an Air Force base. Caterpillar field researchers and product application people followed each machine. Customers were enthusiastic. But, curiously enough, not one of the nine models was for sale. Reason: The Company, in pooling its resources of know-how and experience, was calling on the customer to help build the best "big tractor" ever to come out the back door of a factory.

This was the last hurdle—the one that would top off and test all the work that had gone before. Because, in a sense, the D9 wasn't new at all; it had been evolving on Caterpillar's drawing boards and proving grounds for five years. To start, engineers and sales and service people had discussed specifications and requirements. As time passed, competition and changing customer needs had altered the picture. Five complete versions of the new tractor had been designed—and then killed. Final decision (1950) to go ahead with the D9 meant wooden mock-ups, pilot models, even a new factory.

How much horsepower for the D9 Tractor? Sales, service, research and engineering executives pool their experience.

Smallest, biggest of the Company's crawlers: D2 and D9.

How will the D9 do at 65 below zero? Engineers find out in the research laboratory's cold room.

New
Factories

Manager Naumann and products of Caterpillar's Joliet Plant.

In the nine years following the Second World War, two big factories went up in Peoria; others in Joliet, Illinois, and York, Pennsylvania. Caterpillar acquired the Trackson Company of Milwaukee and established an English subsidiary. Plans called for another plant in Decatur, Illinois. By the end of 1955, over $200 million will have been invested in post-war expansion.

Construction on the largest of the new facilities started in 1949 on a 320-acre tract near Joliet. Built to manufacture the Company's new line of earthmoving equipment, the plant and adjoining parts warehouse include 1.4 million square feet of floor space and over 2,700 employees.

"Our people are striving for customer satisfaction in terms of high quality and low costs," says 43-year-old Bill Naumann, plant manager since January, 1952.

"My chief responsibility is training people to assume additional responsibility . . . that includes myself. Most all of us in Joliet are in positions of increased responsibility . . . the big problem has been training ourselves. The main thing I've learned is how much there is to learn. I'm asking new questions every day."

When he completed high school in 1929, Naumann wanted to go to college, couldn't afford it and "looked for a job where I could get an education." He found it in Caterpillar's four-year machinist apprentice program (starting at 23¢ an hour), plus night school and a three-year correspondence course in mechanical engineering. He spent two years as an inspector, six more as a foreman and general foreman of inspection . . . received five additional factory promotions prior to the Joliet assignment.

Assistant Factory Manager George Armstrong and Naumann check cable control case. The plant manager is a former machinist apprentice and inspector.

A vice president of Joliet's A. of C., Naumann chats with officers Jim Barr and Al Steed. Biggest project to date: Pageant of Progress attended by 140,000.

Gardening with wife, Emma. Naumann's leisure time centers around his home, Bill, Jr. (16), Virginia (12), community activities and technical societies.

CATERPILLAR PEOPLE

*...their achievement
the source of the
Company's strength*

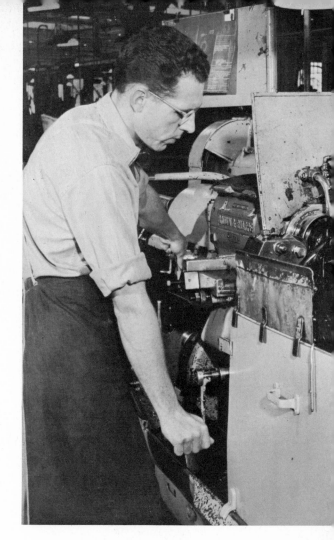

At the San Leandro Plant, Jack Trowbridge

Trowbridge is president of the plant bowling league...

When Jack Trowbridge graduated from high school in 1942, he went to work at Caterpillar's San Leandro (California) Plant because "I knew a lot of people there and they all seemed to like it." Three months later, he climbed into khakis, came home from Europe in 1946 with a corporal's stripes and a wife (Doreen Lloyd of Portsmouth, England).

Returning immediately to San Leandro, Trowbridge applied for the two-year production specialist course.

...attends Trinity Episcopal Church with his family   ...spends $100 monthly for food...

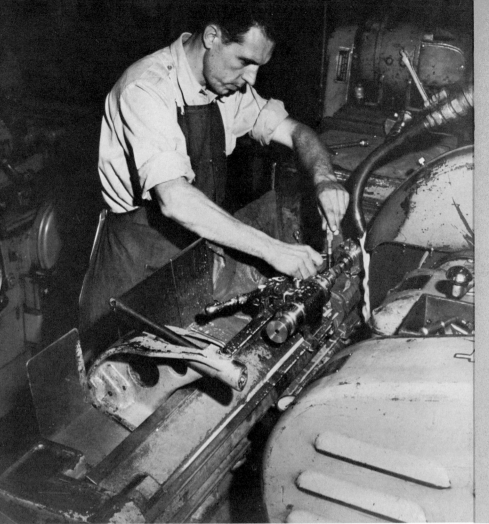

..tomatic screw machine . . .   . . . makes adjustments on a camshaft grinder.

Here, he received training in the set-up and operation of various production machines and attended related classes as well. A journeyman machinist, he usually puts in 40 hours a week. From his pay check, the Company deducts $5.60 each month for $8,000 group life insurance plus weekly disability and accidental death and dismemberment benefits . . . another $7.94 each month for Blue Cross . . . and $9.14 for contributory retirement benefits. Enrollment in each of the plans is voluntary; the Company currently contributes about $8 million yearly to pension and group insurance plans.

With two girls and a boy—all under 10—Trowbridge's monthly budget adds up to $288.04. Groceries ($100) and house payments ($62.54) are the largest items. The family's principal savings are invested in U.S. bonds. Jack also maintains a checking account and saves money in the Caterpillar Credit Union. Among his objectives, security and advancement rate high.

. . . budgets $6 each month for shoes   . . . $62.54 on his San Leandro home . . .   . . . and $15 for gifts and recreation.

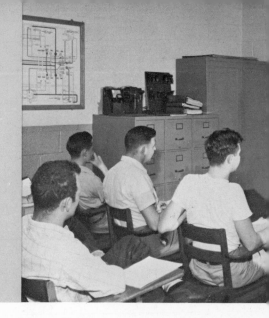

Apprentice machinist Dick Masters (right) learns on-the-job lathe techniques from Caterpillar instructor Ken Star.

Masters (front row, second from left) follows the pointer through a hydraulic sequence circuit.

College graduate trainee Paul Rosenberger will be a design engineer when he completes the orientation program.

Rosenberger's training includes factory assignments; here, he observes a fuel pump adjustment.

Two Trainees

Most machinist apprentices come to Caterpillar directly from high school. Not so with Dick Masters—who spent two years in Bradley University pre-med, another year in the Army Medical Corps, then changed his mind. At the urging of his father, a 25-year employee, he investigated the four-year machinist apprentice program; the Company hired him after careful evaluation of his potential in the manufacturing field.

By the end of the four-year period, Masters will have completed: 100 weeks on drills, lathes and other production machines; 44 weeks of tool room experience;

four weeks on assembly lines, four more as an inspector; 46 weeks of engineering and research work; and about 800 classroom hours of heat treat metallurgy and economics and points in-between. His chances of advancement are good; one-half of his predecessors are now in staff or supervisory positions.

Paul Rosenberger completed his finals at Iowa State University and joined Caterpillar a few days later. After a two-year Army interruption, he resumed his training in the college graduate orientation program. The 24-year-old agricultural engineer chose an engineering

The apprentice works out a hydraulics problem
. . . then tries his solution on this test stand.

At the Peoria proving ground, Rosenberger is taught operation of all Caterpillar equipment.

Two ex-trainees: right, Chuck Woodley, 1930 apprentice graduate and now a vice president; Parts Manager Mark Clements, who completed the college graduate program in 1938.

end-point over a number of other departments — principally sales, sales promotion, manufacturing, service, purchasing, parts and research. Course composition varies with the individual trainee; Rosenberger's, for example, is almost one-half engineering and research projects. He also attends classes, has worked on the proving grounds and a variety of factory locations.

The 17 Caterpillar training programs (3,000 graduates since 1930) operate on the premise that a skilled work force and competent leaders are made, not born. All programs are built around *learning by doing*.

Board Chairman Louis Neumiller (right) and President Harmon Eberhard.

"I'd like you to take a look at this new foundry conveyor set-up."   With Vice President Woodley (left) . . . walking toward the fo

Leadership

Two men stepped briskly out of Peoria's general offices, donned safety glasses, picked up Vice President Chuck Woodley and headed for the foundry. Both had been over the same ground a great many times. They were: Board Chairman Louis B. Neumiller (58) and President Harmon S. Eberhard (54).

Neumiller began his career in Peoria in 1915 as a clerk-stenographer—at a salary of $60 a month. After a short tour of duty in the U.S. Ordnance Corps, he returned to an engineering job, later became parts manager (1925). When the Company unveiled its new diesel line in 1931, he moved to the key position of service manager. Advancing through sales and industrial relations, he became president in late 1941.

Harmon Eberhard succeeded him 12½ years later. Eberhard joined Holt in California in 1916 as a draftsman ($40 monthly), served a one-year hitch in the Corps of Engineers. He was named chief engineer in 1933 . . . stepped up to vice president in charge of research, engineering and manufacturing in 1942. Later (1950), he became executive vice president.

Neumiller and Eberhard have adjacent offices, frequently compare views and ideas. Each quietly occupies a different part of the stage. When *Fortune Magazine* interviewed the two men, "neither claimed personal credit for any one advance or innovation." Nonplused, *Fortune* titled its article "The Art of Modest Management."

"This conveyor is going to boost both efficiency and output."

"Another long-range job is mechanizing this molding floor."

79

The Community

Caterpillar gave both land and construction for this playground.

New East Peoria fire house; Mayor Allison (holding axe) is a Caterpillar employee. The facility can provide emergency service to the Peoria Plant; the Company paid 95% of its cost.

Hard pressed by a last-minute failure of its auditorium electrical facilities, a Peoria County grade school called Caterpillar for help. Within an hour, one of the Company's community relations representatives was on his way with a supply of factory extension cords. After he had the auditorium lighted, a still more serious problem arose: the guest speaker couldn't make it. The representative had an answer: he gave the speech himself.

Contributions of time, goods and cash to organizations concerned with human health and welfare, character building and education are one indication of the Company's readiness to lift on its corner of the civic load. Another example is the emphasis placed on civic affairs. Caterpillar urges employees to take part in beneficial community activities, whether they be committee memberships, governmental affairs or church and club affiliations. Still another example is the Company's plant escort service . . . in Peoria alone, trained escorts guide about 12,000 customers and community friends annually through the various factories.

In these and other good neighbor roles, according to President Eberhard, Caterpillar is simply discharging a responsibility: "The Company is a citizen here—a corporate citizen. It enjoys many of the rights of citizenship . . . it must therefore shoulder a share of the responsibilities."

The Cats

In 1952, an industrial basketball team won the first of three straight National A.A.U. titles. Next, it squeezed by the collegiate champions from Kansas University. Then, with an assist from the Jayhawkers, it polished off all comers in the Helsinki Olympics and rolled over the Russian five in the finals. The team: the Peoria Cats. The players: like Frank McCabe, all Caterpillar employees.

A civil engineer (Marquette University), McCabe joined the Company and the Cats in 1950. In Peoria, he designed steel and concrete factory structures for 2½ years, then enrolled in the college graduate training program. Unless the team was out of town, he put in a full day on the job, then practiced evenings. His basketball days were only a preface to a career—not a career itself; he received the salary normally paid for each job he filled.

The Cats is just one of 16 Company-sponsored activities that range from chess club to mixed chorus. All activities—including the Cats—were first organized by employees themselves. When participating activities so request, the Company provides coordination, basic equipment and a place to meet.

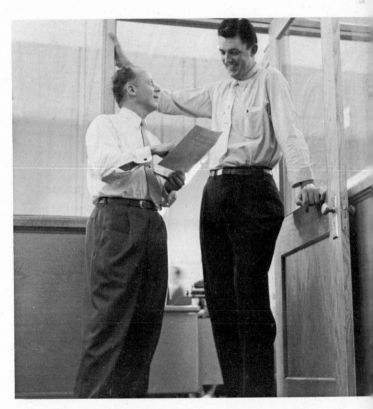

Six-foot eight-inch Frank McCabe and Bill McCoy, manager of sales training. After four straight years as a National A.A.U. All-American, McCabe retired from the squad to spend full time on his new job in the sales training division.

BUSINESS PARTNERS

...as part of each product, the handiwork of other firms

Attica, Indiana, is a tree-shaded, easy-going community located along the tree-shaded, easy-going banks of the Wabash. From its 3,862 population and the area surrounding, 750 people go to work at Harrison Steel Castings Co.; the rest of the town leans heavily on the business Harrison creates. A substantial part of this business has flowed steadily into Peoria since World War I.

Caterpillar counts on some 4,000 vendors whose products come trooping in on approximately 14,000 railroad cars and 28,000 trucks yearly from 44 states. Harrison is one of the oldest of the lot. In 1914, Joseph W. Harrison sold 800 tons of track shoes and related parts to Caterpillar's Peoria predecessor, The Holt Manufacturing Company. So anxious was he to turn out top grade work that he supervised the pouring himself and slept in his office to watch for trouble. In the 40 years after, almost 350,000 tons of steel castings followed along behind.

The three Harrison boys, Roy, Wade and Glen, now run the business. Caterpillar is visited most often by the latter who is vice president in charge of sales. "We're sort of another department of Caterpillar," Glen Harrison admits. "We urge our people to think high quality in terms of your standards. They realize your success is theirs, too. When we see one of your tractors, we see Harrison steel."

The Harrison foundry, including a $1½ million post-war expansion, is pretty much a self-sufficient unit—to the point of quarrying its own molding and core sand a few miles away. Chief among the foundry's floor pieces are three 20-ton open hearth and two new electric furnaces. Facilities include a metallurgical laboratory and a pattern shop. Of an evening, employees can bowl or lounge in the firm's recreation center. They get good wages and split from 10 to 20% of the company's profits at the year's end.

Glen Harrison among Harrison-cast sprockets in Peoria.

Carroll Wallace checks out grinding wheels to Gordon Howard at the Harrison Foundry. Wallace has been mayor of Attica for seven years.

Pouring hot steel from Harrison electric furnace. Samples from each heat are analyzed in metallurgical laboratories in both Attica and Peoria.

Attica, Indiana, home town of Harrison Steel Castings Co.

Vice President Beard and Chief Engineer Simcox check an experimental pull stumper at Fleco's Florida proving ground.

Auxiliary Equipment

Athey Trailer with Cat rubber-tired Tractor. The big dump wagon can run with 30 tons, is reinforced for quarry work.

In 1945, a contractor walked into the Jacksonville office of the Florida Machine and Foundry Co. and asked Superintendent George Peacock about casting a special land clearing rake for one of his crawler tractors. Later the same year, another customer called for a bulldozer-mounted stumper for the same sort of assignment. Recognizing the larger market potential, the Florida firm wondered: Could land clearing equipment be merchandised through an already-established dealer organization? The result was the Florida Land Clearing Equipment Co. (now Fleco Corporation) and a line of 11 devices selling under labels like: stumpers, treedozers, tree cutters, undercutters and rock, root and brush rakes. Fleco retails all 11 through Caterpillar dealers.

A number of comparable firms supply supplementary products for attachment on, behind, or in front of Caterpillar machines. Two others, for example, are the Hyster Company (winches, logging equipment, crawler-mounted excavators) and the Athey Corporation (hauling and loading units). Characteristically, such companies manufacture on a smaller scale than would be

To move huge logs both quickly and economically: Couple a Hyster Winch and Logging Arch to a track-type tractor.

feasible at Caterpillar. And they are well equipped to provide the specialized knowledge, the degree of expertness, that is incorporated in such tools as the Hyster Logging Arch and the Athey Quarry Wagon.

Products join auxiliary equipment lines by both accident and design. In 1948, for example, a Wisconsin contractor ruined a root rake in rocky ground. Fleco brought it back to Jacksonville, had a heavier model engineered and called it a rock rake. Ideas for a tree cutter and a pull stumper originated with two Caterpillar dealers. And Fleco's treedozer is manufactured under a 1952 licensing agreement with Caterpillar.

Manufacturers like Athey, Fleco and Hyster generally engineer their lines for the prime movers of one manufacturer . . . because it simplifies their production problem and broadens research opportunities. Most important, their working arrangement with Caterpillar dealers helps provide them a ready-made sales organization. The Company, in turn, likes the arrangement because such products lengthen the list of uses to which Caterpillar machines may be applied.

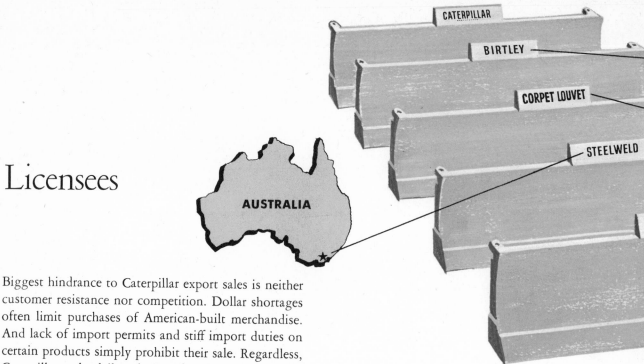

CATERPILLAR
BIRTLEY
CORPET LOUVET
STEELWELD

AUSTRALIA

Licensees

Biggest hindrance to Caterpillar export sales is neither customer resistance nor competition. Dollar shortages often limit purchases of American-built merchandise. And lack of import permits and stiff import duties on certain products simply prohibit their sale. Regardless, Caterpillar seeks daily solutions for two overseas problems: (1) The demand for wealth producing machinery to help construction and/or reconstruction; (2) The demand for matched earthmoving equipment to work with the Company's tractors (which usually cross international barriers with greater ease).

One solution is licensing foreign firms to build and sell "banned" equipment under their own trademarks. An example is Steelweld Pty. Ltd. of Braybrook (near Melbourne), Australia—first to be licensed under the Company's post-war program. Under a 1946 agreement, Steelweld manufactures motor graders, bull-dozers, cable and hydraulic controls and agricultural tool bars . . . then sells through Cat dealers. Like other licensees (The Birtley Company, Ltd., England; Corpet Louvet & Cie., France; Wright Boag & Head Wrightson (Pty.) Ltd., South Africa), Steelweld is free to market its products anywhere in the world.

The four licensees get blueprints, engineering changes and other technical data from Caterpillar . . . as well as ready access to its general experience and know-how. Sales and service methods, even advertisements, are often patterned after those of Caterpillar. Products and parts, says the license agreement, are to duplicate the design and quality of their American cousins. Result? Overseas users can choose both the kind of currency and the country of manufacture for the procurement of such equipment.

Steelweld No. 212 Motor Grader. Caterpillar provides engine and transmission . . . and blueprints for the rest of the machine.

Birtley No. 80 Scraper and D8 Tractor. Products of the old (1819) firm fill English gaps in Caterpillar's product line.

The two trademarks on the front of this South African tractor-dozer symbolize the Caterpillar-licensee partnership.

In the storage lot at Corpet-Louvet's factory, LaCourneuve, Seine, France: New scrapers hitched to Cat DW21 Tractors.

87

Goodloe Yancey—36 years a Caterpillar dealer, 41 years in the equipment business.

...in Yancey's plush "Customer Room"— most conducive to the signing of orders.

ACCENT ON SALES
...*from Montana to Madagascar, a unique organization*

Almost 800 Caterpillar dealer outlets dot the U.S. and every nation of the free world. They sell wealth producing equipment; they back it with round-the-clock service. Of these, the two in Atlanta and Augusta, Georgia, belong to Yancey Bros. Co., one of an independently owned domestic dealer group whose individual net worth averages over $1 million apiece.

In 1918, the Yanceys thought they saw crawler sales possibilities in Georgia. But after cooling their heels for a week in Peoria, they were told: "You can't do it, we've tried." Furthermore, said the Company's sales manager, all new tractors were going direct to the Army. There were, however, 35 non-current models in the yard and if the Yanceys thought they could move them, well go ahead and try ... at 5% commission—or 20% plus a dealer contract if they sold all 35. Armed only with a photograph of the machine, they set sail for Georgia and went to work. By the end of the year, the Peoria lot was empty and a similar one on the West Coast draining fast.

Yancey sales now run to millions yearly. Of this, about two-thirds represents new Caterpillar machines and parts. The remainder comes in from used equipment, service and sales of related lines. For his 84-county territory in northern Georgia, Yancey employs

200 people. He has spent more than $1 million on new facilities since the end of World War II. Included are the Augusta branch (1947) and a new building in Atlanta (1951). The latter is set on a 12-acre site and features a proving ground where used and rebuilt machines are tested before resale.

To speed both sales and service, inventories run high—in excess of $1½ million. Receivables total over $4 million. Terms are arranged to suit customers' income situations. For example, farmers' notes fall due when crops come in. "You have to know bankers real well in this business," says Yancey. "We work closely with our bankers . . . just like our salesmen do with customers."

Goodloe Yancey himself is one of the most enthusiastic Caterpillar boosters in or out of the Company. He has become so closely identified with the yellow painted machines that a few of his customers have the idea he manufactures them. Because his products are profit producers, he will go a long way for a new customer who looks promising. He once gave a former employee a used D6 Tractor (nothing down) to get him started on a farm contracting venture. Six years later, he sold the same man $100,000 worth of heavy equipment.

. . . kibitzing parts orders of customer
K. E. McIntosh, asphalt contractor.

. . . if we bid the D7 and bulldozer,
how high do we go on their old D6?

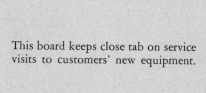

This board keeps close tab on service visits to customers' new equipment.

Serviceman makes adjustments on E. A. Hudson's Sons' new D7 Tractor.

Augusta branch employs 33 people. Manager H. O. Houk stands in doorway.

Product, sales and market data move rapidly from factory to dealer and vice versa. Stationed in the Southeast, these Caterpillar-employed men are primarily responsible. Paul Smith, second from right, is district representative and the Company's chief contact with Yancey and two other dealers. At his right is Special Representative Ken Grimes; he helps dealers with engine sales problems. Rudy Lenich (far right) is a service representative and spends most of his time on customers' jobs. Man in the light coat is Whitey Kern, agricultural representative. All four travel constantly, are generally home only on week-ends.

Jack Thacker (seated, center) is Peoria's assistant eastern sales manager (Southeast). Around him are Merle Dargel, eastern service manager; Bob Talbott, eastern credit manager; Jack Baity, eastern advertising representative; Bernie Grimm, eastern parts manager. Average age—34.

Vice President Don Yancey (left) in Peoria with Alex Justeson, manager of Caterpillar's eastern sales division (of U. S. and Canada).

The Customer

Alex MacDougald, who says he dropped the "ander" from his first name because he had to sign so many checks, insists that his is not an Horatio Alger story. "I never had to get up at four in the morning. I've just figured everything out on a sound mathematical basis. If you do that and surround yourself with good men and good equipment, there's nothing to it."

Whether there is or there isn't, the MacDougald Construction Company has come a long way since 1919. Its lengthy list of completed projects, in addition to roads and streets, includes railroads, bridges, sewage disposal plants, airfields, dry docks, factories, housing projects and hospitals.

Atlanta's largest contractor, MacDougald owns 279 major construction machines—from jackhammers to asphalt pavers. Fifty carry the Caterpillar trademark: track and wheel-type tractors, motor graders, earthmoving tools, electric sets and engines. He maintains an equipment shop in Atlanta, still counts heavily on the dealer for both parts and service. His chief mechanic, Bill Wilson, is a former Yancey employee.

Alex MacDougald built the second concrete highway in Georgia.

MacDougald and Don Yancey inspect the contractor's Atlanta yard.

He has built . . . this section of the Atlanta Expressway.

He is building . . . two miles of bridge approach near Gadsden, Alabama.

He will build . . . talking new equipment with Yancey salesman "Rube" Gunnell.

Agricultural Dealer

Wedged up against the northern border of California are 6,300 square miles of Siskiyou County, four-fifths of which is mountainous and one-half of which is covered with big pine and Douglas fir. Still, it's good cattle country. And there's plenty of room for potatoes, alfalfa, barley and wheat. Siskiyou's county seat (Yreka) is, according to the chamber of commerce, "the hub around which turns the governmental, social and industrial life of an inland empire." At 612 South Main Street in Yreka, there is a bright store belonging to Chico Baumbach, Caterpillar agricultural dealer.

Unlike the full-line Caterpillar merchant, the ag dealer is not a ubiquitous institution. He is located within the regular industrial dealer's territory—but only where the latter is unable to provide farmers with home town agricultural service.

Baumbach began working for Caterpillar dealers in 1929, became a dealer himself 20 years later. In addition to his Caterpillar and John Deere accounts, he carries spray pumps, irrigation pipe, chain saws, cattle chutes, seeders and other farm supplies. Total employment is 11; Baumbach, son Rod and Tom Wray handle sales.

Ag dealer Baumbach calls on customer-rancher Leonard Shelley.

Baumbach shows Shelley a D4 and dozer, later sold him a D7.

The telephone jangled impatiently in the home of Bud Balch, manager of the Indianapolis Parts Depot. It was 11 p.m. Balch rubbed the sleep from his eyes, answered an emergency Paducah call from Whayne Supply Company, Caterpillar's Kentucky dealer. A contractor, it developed, needed a rarely-called-for hydraulic cylinder group for his bulldozer . . . and he needed it quickly.

Balch drove the 10 miles to his depot . . . then checked bus, train, truck and air schedules, settled on the latter. Back in the storeroom, he wrestled a 236-pound, prepacked box into the trunk of his car . . . then headed

Parts Depot
... S. O. S.

Loading emergency parts order at Indianapolis Airport.

for Indianapolis Airport. By 1 a.m., he was back in bed. Next morning, the cylinder group was installed and the machine operating.

Dealers carry extensive parts inventories at both main stores and branches . . . but they can scarcely stock each of the Company's 80,000-odd parts in quantity and still leave room for the boss's office. So strategically situated depots—10 of them—store slow moving items and other categories in which dealers may occasionally be caught short. Emergency orders from the U.S., Canada, Alaska and even overseas get rapid-fire, round-the-clock depot attention.

Indianapolis Parts Depot personnel. M. L. Balch (center) is manager. In back of him are Assistant Manager Howie Williams and Storeroom Foreman Jim Stum. Dealers have phone numbers of all three, frequently rout them out of bed.

95

Export Dealer

Its territory is huge (2½ times the size of Texas). Many of its customers are relatively isolated. Its machines are operated longer than is usually the case in the U.S. Therefore, from Iringa to Mbale, the emphasis lies heavily on service at Gailey and Roberts Limited. From home office Nairobi, the East African firm runs 14 well equipped branches in Kenya Colony and the protectorates of Uganda and Tanganyika. Eleven of these offer Caterpillar parts and service.

As old as the track-type tractor, G & R introduced the crawler to British East Africa in 1924, got into the earthmoving business on a larger scale in the early thirties. It employs 2,175 people. In addition to the Caterpillar account (one third of its business), it represents a long roll of agricultural, construction, mining and logging machinery manufacturers.

G & R originated in 1904 when J. H. Gailey and D. O. Roberts hung their signboard on a wood and iron shack along Nairobi's Government Road. Mustached in the Edwardian style, the young men had seen the country, lived among the natives, helped plan and survey a railway to link the Indian Ocean with Lake Victoria. Tools and equipment, they knew, would be needed to open up the virgin land. They started with harness and plows, buckets and nails, spades and building materials.

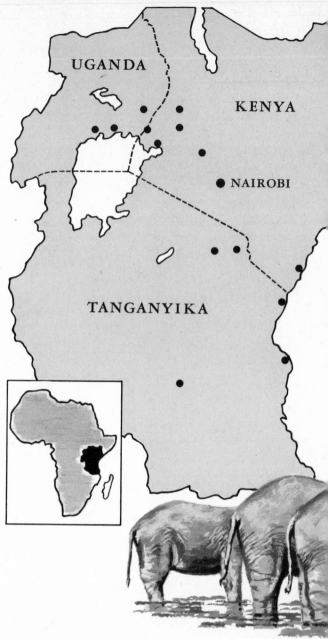

Cat DW21 and No. 21 Scraper working around Sasamua Dam. The new structure will provide additional water for Nairobi, 60 miles distant.

No. 212 Motor Grader rewo

G & R branch in Dar es Salaam, Tanganyika.

Sales manager J. M. L. Brown talks with G & R personnel and D4 prospects. Because of Mau Mau trouble, all are armed (including Caterpillar District Representative Verhyden who took the photograph).

near Mombasa, Kenya.

G & R customer East African Railways & Harbours is moving 10 million cubic yards of earth on a 209-mile railroad extension in Western Uganda.

Two Cat Diesel Engines drilling for oil in West Texas.

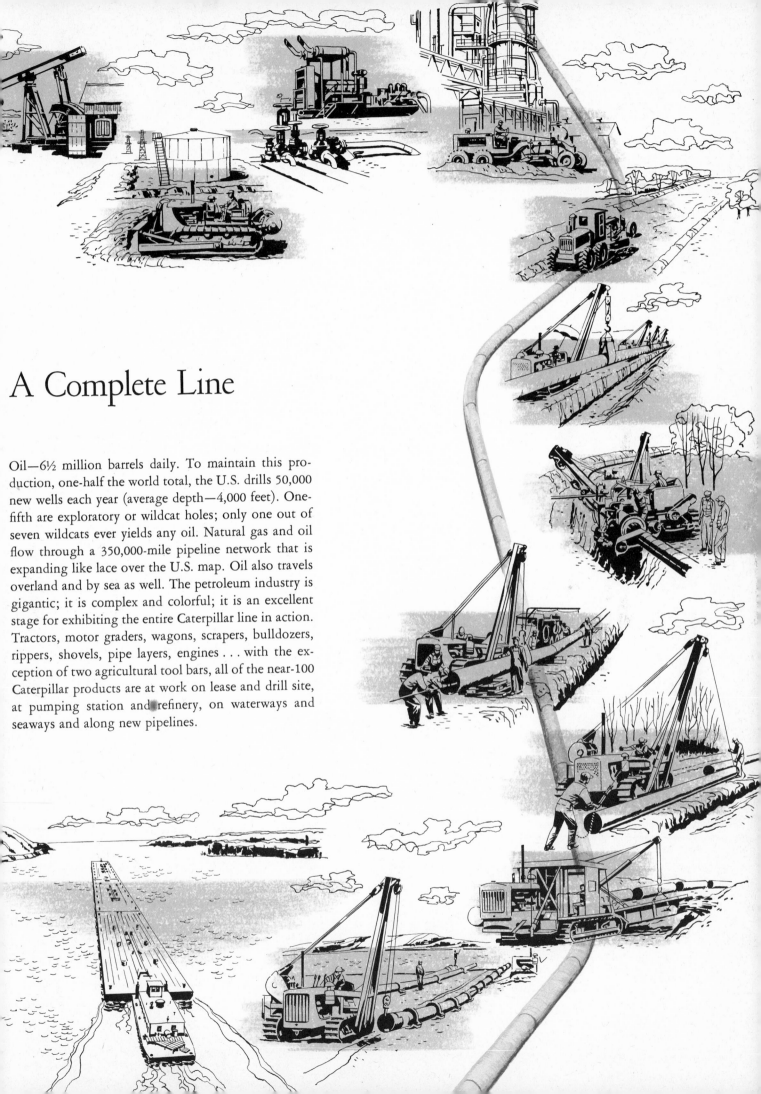

A Complete Line

Oil—6½ million barrels daily. To maintain this production, one-half the world total, the U.S. drills 50,000 new wells each year (average depth—4,000 feet). One-fifth are exploratory or wildcat holes; only one out of seven wildcats ever yields any oil. Natural gas and oil flow through a 350,000-mile pipeline network that is expanding like lace over the U.S. map. Oil also travels overland and by sea as well. The petroleum industry is gigantic; it is complex and colorful; it is an excellent stage for exhibiting the entire Caterpillar line in action. Tractors, motor graders, wagons, scrapers, bulldozers, rippers, shovels, pipe layers, engines . . . with the exception of two agricultural tool bars, all of the near-100 Caterpillar products are at work on lease and drill site, at pumping station and refinery, on waterways and seaways and along new pipelines.

Winning entry . . . California . . . bought in 1918, now operated 100 days yearly. Original owner C. C. Neilson still gets service and new parts for this Holt "75" from his Cat dealer.

No Orphans

Early in 1954, Caterpillar announced an unusual contest for dealer salesmen. They were to photograph the oldest operating crawlers in their territories, then send photos and accompanying data sheets to Peoria.

From 40 U.S. states, seven Canadian provinces and 14 lands overseas, entries rolled in for Caterpillar machines—and those built by predecessors Best and Holt. There was, for example, a Holt "60"—vintage 1914—still clearing and plowing new land in Alberta, Canada. And the first diesel crawler delivered (1931) to Puerto Rico . . . operated 16 years by Domingo Aponte, then by his brother, now by his son. And the D6 that slipped into a bomb crater in a broken Dutch dike in 1945, sat four years under 30 feet of earth . . . then was dug up by a farmer and put to work in less than a week. Contest judges (including President Eberhard) picked out winners on a basis of machine age and quality of photo and story.

Much of the long machine life evident in each entry is the result of the Company's attitude that old machines not only never die . . . but also need not fade away. "Never a Caterpillar orphan," say parts people . . . and prove their point with daily parts shipments for combines and tractors out of production for decades. Though the names of forerunners Best and Holt were dropped from new tractors in 1925, there are so many of them still operating that Caterpillar regularly gets inquiries addressed to both firms.

Second place . . . Tunisia . . . Caterpillar 10-Ton Tractor . . . served in First World War, went to present owner in 1921. He hid it in a scrap pile during German World War II occupation.

Expanding Market

Caterpillar's market development is supposed to increase sales, yes—and it usually has another, equally important purpose: to remind listeners and readers of a bad situation that can be remedied. One example: a sanitary landfill program sponsored jointly with Kiwanis International; objective—turn municipal garbage dumps into productive, usable land. Another example: the need for new roads.

In 1950, the American Association of State Highway Officials placed the cost of modernizing U.S. roads at $29 billion. After three years of stepped-up construction, the Association again tallied the score . . . and found the Nation $35 billion behind! Conclusion: Present roadbuilding falls far short of the mark . . . U.S. roads are crumbling faster than they're being built. And the number of vehicles on them keeps increasing, has almost doubled since World War II.

Worst aspect of an inadequate road system is not the cost—which approximates $3¾ billion yearly in wasted fuel, excessive wear, accidents. More shocking is the regularity with which the motor vehicle kills and maims its way across the land. Caterpillar ads like the one below stress the good roads theme, urge readers to back sound highway programs with votes and tax dollars.

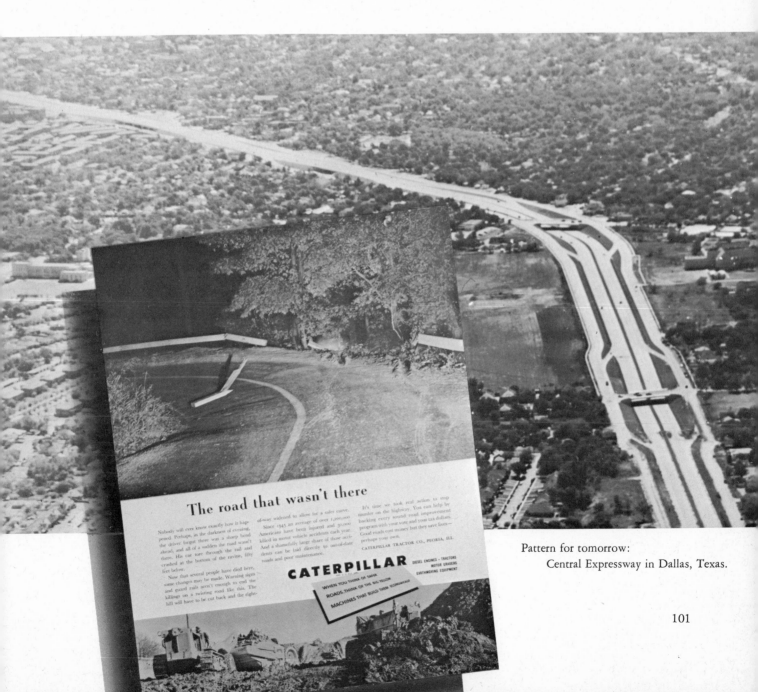

Pattern for tomorrow:
Central Expressway in Dallas, Texas.

AND so you've had a glimpse of Caterpillar — dramatic proof that necessity *is* the mother of invention. First the combined harvester and the futility of big wheels; then the birth of the crawler. The new gasoline tractors and the change to diesel power. The emancipation of the work animal and two tragic, world-shattering conflicts. The greatness of the machine in peace; its necessity and strength in war. And people, the most vital ingredient of success. The shareholders who supply the capital and shoulder the risk. The men and women and their tools; the managers; the suppliers, the other business friends; the world family of dealers and the boss over all, the customer. The authors have labored not to spotlight separate men... were they to do so, the stage would be too large and the story too long. Other than the founders, where individuals have been identified, they serve as examples. Credit belongs not to the one or the few... but to the many. It is the aim of this closing signature to acknowledge in fullest measure their great contribution.

Printed in the United States of America

The trademarks CATERPILLAR *and* CAT
are registered throughout the world

For the most part, photographs for this book were taken by Caterpillar people or selected
from the Company's historical files. In addition, the Company is grateful to Bettmann Archives for the
upper-right photo on p. 30 . . . to the United Press for the following photos: p. 25, lower left; p. 27,
center right; p. 30, lower right; p. 42, upper left, upper right; p. 43, lower right; p. 48, upper right; p. 56, lower left, lower
right; p. 101, center . . . and to Acme for: p. 30, center right; p. 43, upper left; p. 49, upper left, upper
right; p. 51, lower right; p. 53, lower right. The cartoon on p. 17 is reprinted with special permission of the artist,
Fontaine Fox, and the Bell Syndicate, Inc. With the exception of the Bettmann, United Press and Acme
prints, limited numbers of all photos are available from Caterpillar upon request. Professional associations,
educators and members of the press are encouraged to utilize this service as well as the information in this book.

Research and writing / *Staff, Caterpillar Tractor Co.*
Design / *Grant-Jacoby Studios, Inc., Chicago, Illinois*
Printing / *Photopress, Inc., Chicago, Illinois*